Teacher's Program Overview

Scott Foresman-Addison Wesley

enVisionMATH®

Common Core

Authors

Randall I. Charles
Professor Emeritus
Department of Mathematics
San Jose State University
San Jose, California

Janet H. Caldwell
Professor of Mathematics
Rowan University
Glassboro, New Jersey

Mary Cavanagh
Executive Director of Center for Practice, Research, and Innovation in Mathematics Education (PRIME)
Arizona State University
Mesa, Arizona

Juanita Copley
Professor Emerita, College of Education
University of Houston
Houston, Texas

Warren D. Crown
Professor Emeritus of Mathematics Education
Graduate School of Education
Rutgers University
New Brunswick, New Jersey

Francis (Skip) Fennell
L. Stanley Bowlsbey Professor of Education and Graduate and Professional Studies
McDaniel College
Westminster, Maryland

Stuart J. Murphy
Visual Learning Specialist
Boston, Massachusetts

Kay B. Sammons
Coordinator of Elementary Mathematics
Howard County Public Schools
Ellicott City, Maryland

Jane F. Schielack
Professor of Mathematics
Associate Dean for Assessment and Pre K–12 Education, College of Science
Texas A&M University
College Station, Texas

William F. Tate IV
Edward Mallinckrodt Distinguished University Professor in Arts & Sciences
Washington University
St. Louis, Missouri

PEARSON

Glenview, Illinois • Boston, Massachusetts • Chandler, Arizona • Upper Saddle River, New Jersey

Grant Wiggins
Researcher and Educational Consultant
Hopewell, New Jersey

Mathematicians

David M. Bressoud
DeWitt Wallace Professor of Mathematics
Macalester College
St. Paul, Minnesota

Roger Howe
Professor of Mathematics
Yale University
New Haven, Connecticut

Gary Lippman
Professor of Mathematics and Computer Science
California State University East Bay
Hayward, California

ELL Consultant

Jim Cummins
Professor
The University of Toronto
Toronto, Canada

Elizabeth Baker
Mathematics Coordinator
Gilbert Public Schools
Gilbert, Arizona

Amy Barber
K–12 Math Coach
Peninsula School District ESC
Gig Harbor, Washington

Laura Cua
Teacher
Columbus City Schools
Columbus, Ohio

Wafa Deeb-Westervelt
Assistant Superintendent for Curriculum, Instruction, and Professional Development
Freeport Public Schools
Freeport, New York

Lynn Gullette
Title 1 Math Intervention
Mobile County Public Schools
Gilliard Elementary
Mobile, Alabama

Beverly K. Kimes
Director of Mathematics
Birmingham City Schools
Birmingham, Alabama

Kelly O'Rourke
Elementary School Assistant Principal
Clark County School District
Las Vegas, Nevada

Piper L. Riddle
Evidence-Based Learning Specialist
Canyons School District
Sandy, Utah

Debra L. Vitale
Math Coach
Bristol Public Schools
Bristol, Connecticut

Diane T. Wehby
Math Support Teacher
Birmingham City Schools
Birmingham, Alabama

ISBN-13: 978-0-328-67265-3
ISBN-10: 0-328-67265-3

3 4 5 6 7 8 9 10 V003 15 14 13 12

Contents

Content Guide

Program Guide

About the Authors

Randall I. Charles
Professor Emeritus
Department of Mathematics
San Jose State University
San Jose, California

Randall Charles has teaching experience at all levels, and was a K–12 mathematics supervisor for five years. He is the former Vice President of the National Council of Supervisors of Mathematics. He was a member of the NCTM Research Advisory Committee, and has authored or edited many publications for NCTM. He was a member of the writing team for the NCTM Curriculum Focal Points.

Much of Randy's writing and research have focused on problem solving. He was the senior author on a widely-used series called *Problem Solving Experiences in Mathematics*. He is a senior author with Pearson Scott Foresman and Pearson Prentice Hall where he has authored more than 100 textbooks for grades K–college.

Janet H. Caldwell
Professor of Mathematics
Rowan University
Glassboro, New Jersey

Janet Caldwell teaches mathematics and directs projects providing professional development to teachers of mathematics. She has received a Professor of the Year Award and a Distinguished Teaching Award.

Mary Cavanagh
Executive Director of Center for Practice, Research, and Innovation in Mathematics Education (PRIME)
Arizona State University
Mesa, Arizona

Mary Cavanagh works with English language learners, their families, and teachers. Her most recent work includes developing a model math and science curriculum and professional development for after-school programs.

Stuart J. Murphy
Visual Learning Specialist
Boston, Massachusetts

Stuart Murphy works in the field of visual learning and is the author of the 63-book *MathStart* series. He is part of the authorship team of the Pearson Prentice Hall High School mathematics program and *digits*, Pearson Education's new Middle Grades mathematics program. He is also the author of *I SEE I LEARN*, a series of storybooks for Pre-Kindergarten children.

Kay B. Sammons
Coordinator of Elementary Mathematics
Howard County Public Schools
Ellicott City, Maryland

Kay Sammons is responsible for development of curriculum and assessment. She provides professional development for teachers in the areas of curriculum implementation, pedagogy, assessment, and intervention.

Juanita V. Copley
Professor Emerita
College of Education
University of Houston
Houston, Texas

Nita Copley researches professional development models for early childhood teachers and young children's understanding of mathematical concepts, especially word problems and problem-solving strategies.

Jane F. Schielack
Professor of Mathematics
Associate Dean for Assessment and Pre K–12 Education, College of Science
Texas A&M University
College Station, Texas

Janie Schielack works with preservice and inservice teachers to improve their understanding of the mathematical knowledge needed for teaching. She was the Chair of the writing team for the NCTM Curriculum Focal Points.

Janie was a member of the Common Core State Standards NCTM Review/Input Group.

Warren D. Crown
Professor Emeritus of Mathematics Education
Graduate School of Education
Rutgers University
New Brunswick, New Jersey

Warren Crown has designed educational software for classroom use, and has worked as an educator of mathematics teachers at Rutgers for the past 30 years.

William F. Tate IV
Edward Mallinckrodt
Distinguished University Professor in Arts & Sciences
Washington University
St. Louis, Missouri

Bill Tate is known for his research focused on the social determinates of mathematics education attainment and disparities. He is the recipient of a presidential citation from the American Educational Research Association for his conceptual and methodological contributions to the opportunity to learn literature.

Francis (Skip) Fennell
L. Stanley Bowlsbey Professor of Education and Graduate and Professional Studies
McDaniel College
Westminster, Maryland

Skip Fennell is a mathematics educator and has experience as a classroom teacher, a principal, and a supervisor of instruction. He is currently the L. Stanley Bowlsbey Professor of Education and Graduate and Professional Studies at McDaniel College (note to reader: this is an endowed chair) and a past President of the National Council of Teachers of Mathematics.

Skip was a member of the writing teams for the Principles and Standards for School Mathematics (NCTM, 2000), Curriculum Focal Points (NCTM, 2006), and the Common Core State Standards (CCSSO, 2010). He also served as a member of the National Mathematics Advisory Panel from May 2006 to April 2008.

Focus and Coherence

by Randall I. Charles

> *"...what and how students are taught should reflect not only the topics that fall within a certain academic discipline, but also the key ideas that determine how knowledge is organized and generated within that discipline."*
>
> Common Core State Standards Initiative 2010, p. 3

The **Common Core State Standards** (CCSS), released in June 2010, represent the work of numerous mathematicians and mathematics educators concerned about the state of K–12 mathematics education in the United States. A primary goal of the developers of the CCSS was to respond to the criticism of mathematics curricula in the United States being a mile wide and an inch deep by providing a roadmap to "more ***focused and coherent*** [curricula] in order to improve mathematics achievement in this country" (Common Core State Standards Initiative, 2010, p. 3). *enVisionMATH Common Core* fully embraces the focus and coherence called for in the CCSS, and expands upon them in a significant way.

A focused and coherent mathematics curriculum provides in-depth instruction on a limited number of important categories of mathematics content. The CCSS identifies and organizes these important categories of mathematics content standards, to which *enVisionMATH Common Core* is directly aligned, and calls them critical areas. The grade-specific critical areas further organize related content into domains, and each domain organizes related content standards into clusters (see pages 8 and 9). Every lesson and topic in *enVisionMATH Common Core* correlates to the critical areas, domains, and content clusters.

enVisionMATH Common Core is unique in that it extends focus and coherence beyond just providing in-depth instruction on a limited number of important categories of mathematics content. The program extends focus and coherence by making explicit the Big Ideas in mathematics that students need to know and by showing how those ideas are related. A Big Idea in mathematics (called a Key Idea in the CCSS) is a statement of an *idea* that is central to learning mathematics; it links numerous smaller ideas (called ***Essential Understandings*** in *enVisionMATH Common Core)* into a coherent whole (Charles 2005). *enVisionMATH Common Core* connects all CCSS content standards to **Big Ideas** and **Essential Understandings**.

Big Ideas in *enVisionMATH Common Core* run across critical areas and grades; they connect ideas across content topics, and this is one reason they are "big." To illustrate this, the Big Idea called *Equivalence* is outlined on the next page, showing how it correlates to the content standards and to Essential Understandings across grades.

To convey the power of Big Ideas to students, they are translated into student-friendly **Essential Questions** presented at the beginning of each topic. Essential Questions focus students' attention on what they will be learning throughout a topic and what they will be able to do and understand at the end of a topic.

Big Idea: Equivalence

Any number, measure, numerical expression, algebraic expression, or equation can be represented in an infinite number of ways that have the same value.

Content Standards	Related Essential Understandings
K.OA.3 Decompose numbers less than or equal to 10 into pairs. . . .	• There is more than one way to show a number.
1.OA.6 Add and subtract within 20. . . .	• The number 10 can be broken into parts of the whole in different ways.
2.MD.8 Solve word problems involving dollar bills, quarters, dimes, nickels, and pennies. . . .	• The same amount of money can often be represented using different combinations of coins and bills.
3.NBT.2 Fluently add and subtract within 1000. . . .	• An equation shows a balance between what is on the right side and what is on the left side of the equal sign.
4.NBT.5 Multiply a whole number . . . by a one-digit whole number. . . .	• Different numerical expressions can have the same value. Or, the value of one expression can be less than (or greater than) the value of the other expression.
5.NBT.7 Add, subtract, multiply, and divide decimals to hundredths. . . .	• A number divided by a decimal can be represented as an equivalent calculation using place value to change the divisor to a whole number.
6.RP.3 Use ratio and rate reasoning to solve real-world and mathematical problems. . . .	• A part of a whole or a part of a set can be represented by a fraction, a decimal, and a percent.

Conclusion: Why do focus and coherence matter?

A focused and coherent mathematics curriculum makes possible in-depth student understanding, which in turn leads to higher student achievement. Knowing that the myriad of content topics in the high school mathematics curriculum coalesce into six conceptual categories helps students understand mathematics—they see the "whole," not just the "parts." And, when students know that mathematics is grounded on Big Ideas, not just skills, and that those ideas are connected, they better understand mathematics. *enVisionMATH Common Core* embraces and enhances the focus and coherence vision of the CCSS, leading to higher achievement for all.

> "enVisionMATH Common Core *organizes content using exactly the same structure as the Standards for Mathematical Content. Topics are organized by Domain, and all Topics for each Domain are grouped together. The focus and coherence provided by this structure allow* enVisionMATH Common Core *to cultivate both the procedures and the understanding called for in the Common Core State Standards.*"

References

Charles, Randall I. "Big Ideas and Understandings as the Foundation for Elementary and Middle School Mathematics." Journal of Mathematics Education Leadership, 8 no.1 (2005): 9–24.

Common Core State Standards Initiative. Common Core State Standards for Mathematics. Washington, D.C., 2010.

Critical Areas	Domains	Clusters
Representing and comparing whole numbers, initially with sets of objects	**K.CC** Counting and Cardinality	**Know number names and the count sequence.** Standards: K.CC.1, K.CC.2, K.CC.3 **Count to tell the number of objects.** Standards: K.CC.4, K.CC.5 **Compare numbers.** Standards: K.CC.6, K.CC.7
	K.OA Operations and Algebraic Thinking	**Understand addition as putting together and adding to, and understand subtraction as taking apart and taking from.** Standards: K.OA.1, K.OA.2, K.OA.3, K.OA.4, K.OA.5
	K.NBT Number and Operations in Base Ten	**Work with numbers 11–19 to gain foundations for place value.** Standard: K.NBT.1
Describing shapes and space	**K.MD** Measurement and Data	**Describe and compare measurable attributes.** Standards: K.MD.1, K.MD.2 **Classify objects and count the number of objects in each category.** Standard: K.MD.3
	K.G Geometry	**Identify and describe shapes (squares, circles, triangles, rectangles, hexagons, cubes, cones, cylinders, and spheres).** Standards: K.G.1, K.G.2, K.G.3 **Analyze, compare, create, and compose shapes.** Standards: K.G.4, K.G.5, K.G.6

The alignment of Critical Areas with Domains and Clusters is not straightforward in some cases.
This chart shows one interpretation for Grade K.

Grade K Topics	Grade K Big Ideas
Topic 1 One to Five **Topic 2** Comparing and Ordering 0 to 5 **Topic 3** Six to Ten **Topic 4** Comparing and Ordering Numbers 0 to 10 **Topic 5** Numbers to 20 **Topic 6** Numbers to 100	• Number Uses, Classification, and Representation • Numbers and the Number Line • The Base-Ten Numeration System • Comparison and Relationships • Patterns, Relations, and Functions • Practices, Processes, and Proficiencies
Topic 7 Understanding Addition **Topic 8** Understanding Subtraction **Topic 9** More Addition and Subtraction	• Equivalence • Operation Meanings and Relationships • Practices, Processes, and Proficiencies
Topic 10 Composing Numbers 11 to 19 **Topic 11** Decomposing Numbers 11 to 19	• Number Uses, Classification, and Representation • The Base-Ten Numeration System • Practices, Processes, and Proficiencies
Topic 12 Measurement **Topic 13** Sorting, Classifying, Counting, and Categorizing Data	• Comparison and Relationships • Geometric Figures • Data Collection and Representation • Practices, Processes, and Proficiencies
Topic 14 Identifying and Describing Shapes **Topic 15** Position and Location of Shapes **Topic 16** Analyzing, Comparing, and Composing Shapes	• Comparison and Relationships • Geometric Figures • Practices, Processes, and Proficiencies

Content Focus and Coherence: Big Ideas

Big Ideas	Grade K Topics	Grade 1 Topics	Grade 2 Topics	Grade 3 Topics	Grade 4 Topics	Grade 5 Topics	Grade 6 Topics
1 **Number Uses, Classification, and Representation** Numbers can be used for different purposes, and numbers can be classified and represented in different ways.	1, 2, 3, 5, 6, 11	3, 7, 8	5, 10	1	11	1, 3, 9	1, 5, 7
2 **Numbers and the Number Line** The set of real numbers is infinite and ordered. Whole numbers, integers, and fractions are real numbers. Each real number can be associated with a unique point on the number line.	4	16	8, 9	1, 9, 10	12, 13	2, 9, 10	5, 6,10
3 **The Base-Ten Numeration System** The base-ten numeration system is a scheme for recording numbers using digits 0–9, groups of ten, and place value.	6, 10	7, 8, 9	5, 10	1	3, 13	1, 7	1
4 **Equivalence** Any number, measure, numerical expression, algebraic expression, or equation can be represented in an infinite number of ways that have the same value.	9	3, 8	12, 13	2, 8, 10	4, 6, 11, 12, 13	4, 7, 8, 9, 10, 11	1, 3, 5, 6, 14, 16
5 **Comparison and Relationships** Numbers, expressions, measures, and objects can be compared and related to other numbers, expressions, measures, and objects in different ways.	2, 4, 12, 15	4, 9, 12	2, 3, 5, 10, 15	1, 10	3, 11, 13	1, 7	1, 12
6 **Operation Meanings and Relationships** There are multiple interpretations of addition, subtraction, multiplication, and division of rational numbers, and each operation is related to other operations.	7, 8, 9	1, 2, 3, 4, 6	1, 3, 4, 9, 15	2, 4, 6, 7, 8	1, 9, 10, 12	10, 11	8, 9
7 **Estimation** Numbers can be approximated by numbers that are close. Numerical calculations can be approximated by replacing numbers with other numbers that are close and easy to compute with mentally. Some measurements can be approximated using known referents as the unit in the measurement process.			14	2, 9	3, 4, 5, 7, 9, 10, 14	2, 3, 4, 5, 6, 7, 9, 10, 11	3, 7, 8, 9, 14, 15
8 **Properties** For a given set of numbers there are relationships that are always true, called properties, and these are the rules that govern arithmetic and algebra.		1, 5	2, 8	2, 3, 4, 6, 8	1	3, 8	2, 4
9 **Basic Facts and Algorithms** There is more than one algorithm for each of the operations with rational numbers. Some strategies for basic facts and most algorithms for operations with rational numbers, both mental math and paper and pencil, use equivalence to transform calculations into simpler ones.		4, 5, 10, 11	2, 3, 6, 7, 8, 9, 10, 11, 14	2, 3, 6	1, 4, 5, 6, 7, 8, 10, 12	2, 3, 4, 5, 6, 7, 9, 10	2, 3, 7, 8, 9, 16
10 **Variable** Mathematical situations and structures can be translated and represented abstractly using variables, expressions, and equations.				8	1	8	2

Big Ideas	Grade K Topics	Grade 1 Topics	Grade 2 Topics	Grade 3 Topics	Grade 4 Topics	Grade 5 Topics	Grade 6 Topics
11 **Solving Equations and Inequalities** Rules of arithmetic and algebra can be used together with notions of equivalence to transform equations and inequalities so solutions can be found.						8	1, 3, 4, 7, 9, 15
12 **Ratio and Proportionality** When mathematical or real-world quantities have a relationship that can be stated as "for every *x* units of the first quantity there are *y* units of the second quantity," this relationship can be described using a ratio. Proportionality involves a relationship in which the ratio of two quantities remains constant as the corresponding values of the quantities change. In a proportional relationship there are an infinite number of ratios equal to the lowest terms or constant ratio.							12, 13, 14, 15
13 **Patterns, Relations, and Functions** Relationships can be described and generalizations made for mathematical situations that have numbers or objects that repeat in predictable ways. For some relationships, mathematical expressions and equations can be used to describe how members of one set are related to members of a second set.	6	1, 7	5, 6, 7, 10	5	1, 2, 5, 7, 9, 14	2, 3, 4, 5, 6, 8, 16	1, 2, 5, 15
14 **Geometric Figures** Two- and three-dimensional objects with or without curved surfaces can be described, classified, and analyzed by their attributes. An object's location in space can be described quantitatively.	13, 14, 16	15	12	11	16	12, 15, 16	10,11, 18
15 **Measurement** Some attributes of objects are measurable and can be quantified using unit amounts.		12, 13	13, 15, 16	12, 13 14, 15	14, 15, 16	13	16, 17, 18
16 **Data Collection and Representation** Some questions can be answered by collecting and analyzing data, and the question to be answered determines the data that need to be collected and how best to collect the data. Data can be represented visually using tables, charts, and graphs. The type of data determines the best choice of visual representation.	13	14	16	16	15	14	19
17 **Data Distribution** There are special numerical measures that describe the center and spread of numerical data sets. The most appropriate measures for a situation depend on the nature of the data and on the use to be made of the measures.							19
18 **Practices, Processes, and Proficiencies** Mathematics content and practices can be applied to solve problems.	1–16	1–16	1–16	1–16	1–16	1–16	1–19

Critical Content Areas

(1) Representing and comparing whole numbers, initially with sets of objects;

(2) Describing shapes and space. More learning time in Kindergarten should be devoted to number than to other topics.

Kindergarteners begin their study of mathematics with a primary focus on counting and cardinality and number and operation. They count to 100 by ones and tens, and write numbers (numerals) to 20. They solve quantitative problems by counting, comparing, and joining and separating sets, all of which help them develop the foundational understanding for addition and subtraction.

Students model problems using a range of visual representations and in some cases, expressions or equations. They choose and apply strategies to answer quantitative questions and come to recognize the cardinality of small sets of objects (i.e., subitize).

A second area of focus for Kindergarteners is on describing objects using geometric ideas. Students describe shapes by their attributes, orientation, and spatial location. Students name, identify, describe, and compose two- and three-dimensional shapes. In addition, they use spatial reasoning to create models of objects and to compose complex shapes.

New Approaches

Perhaps the most significant adjustment in Kindergarten is the dominant emphasis on number. The **Common Core State Standards** place the development of a strong foundation for number and operations at the core of early mathematics education. To achieve this foundation, students compose and decompose numbers within 20 to help them build an informal understanding of place value and strategies for addition and subtraction.

...students compose and decompose numbers within 20 to help them build an informal understanding of place value ...

The emphasis on counting and cardinality leads to fluency with counting and the ability to determine a quantity without counting (i.e., subitize). According to research (National Research Council, 2009), recognizing small quantities is a precursor to understanding part-part-whole relationships and to developing a sense of number.

The representation of numbers and quantities is expanded with the Kindergarten standards. Students model quantitative relationships with fingers, objects, mental images, generalized drawings, expressions, verbal explanations, and equations. The standards suggest that these representations, especially the equations, be given in a variety of ways so students can develop in depth the number and operations concepts.

Students model quantitative relationships with fingers, objects, mental images, generalized drawings, expressions, verbal explanations, and equations.

In geometry, spatial orientation and relationships are part of the standards, as are modeling, drawing, and building two- and three-dimensional shapes. The recent research on geometry and success later in school indicate the importance of a strong geometric foundation, which the CCSS look to develop in students.

What's Different?

Unlike many state curriculum frameworks, the **Common Core State Standards** do not present a spiral curriculum in which students revisit numerous topics from one year to the next with progressively more complex study. Rather, the CCSS identify a limited number of topics at each grade level, allowing enough time for students to achieve mastery of these concepts. The subsequent year of study builds on the concepts of the previous year. While some review of topics from earlier grades is appropriate and encouraged, the CCSS writers argue that reteaching of these topics should not be needed.

Certain topics that have often been part of the Kindergarten mathematics curriculum are not included in the CCSS. Among the most noticeable are the absence of the study of patterns, money, measurement topics, such as time and calendar, and probability concepts.

- **Patterns** The study of patterns (e.g., shape patterns, sound patterns, kinesthetic patterns) is not an explicit part of the CCSS content standards; however, the Mathematical Practices (specifically 7 and 8) emphasize the importance of recognizing and interacting with patterns as they relate to all domains of mathematics, leading to a more integrated approach to the study of patterns in mathematics.

- **Measurement** Students first tell time in Grade 1; the study of calendar is not part of the CCSS for Mathematics.

- **Geometry** The CCSS introduce the study of symmetry in Grade K and congruence in Grade 8.

- **Probability** Students first encounter probability concepts in Grade 7.

Common Core

Standards for Mathematical Practice

- ✔ Make sense of problems and persevere in solving them.
- ✔ Reason abstractly and quantitatively.
- ✔ Construct viable arguments and critique the reasoning of others.
- ✔ Model with mathematics.
- ✔ Use appropriate tools strategically.
- ✔ Attend to precision.
- ✔ Look for and make use of structure.
- ✔ Look for and express regularity in repeated reasoning.

Grade K Domain Colors

Domain: Counting and Cardinality
Topics: 1, 2, 3, 4, 5, and 6

Domain: Operations and Algebraic Thinking
Topics: 7, 8, and 9

Domain: Number and Operations in Base Ten
Topics: 10 and 11

Domain: Measurement and Data
Topics: 12 and 13

Domain: Geometry
Topics: 14, 15, and 16

Pacing Guide A Program Paced for Success

+ 16 tests/assessments
126 lessons
test + intro new topic/domain in same day

The pacing supports 1 lesson per day. There are 110 grade-level lessons and 10 Step-Up lessons to prepare for next year. Additional time may be spent on review, remediation, differentiation, formative and summative assessment as needed.

7 days	**Topic 1**	One to Five
9 days	**Topic 2**	Comparing and Ordering 0 to 5
7 days	**Topic 3**	Six to Ten
10 days	**Topic 4**	Comparing and Ordering Numbers 0 to 10
5 days	**Topic 5**	Numbers to 20
6 days	**Topic 6**	Numbers to 100
7 days	**Topic 7**	Understanding Addition
8 days	**Topic 8**	Understanding Subtraction
9 days	**Topic 9**	More Addition and Subtraction
4 days	**Topic 10**	Composing Numbers 11 to 19
5 days	**Topic 11**	Decomposing Numbers 11 to 19
8 days	**Topic 12**	Measurement
7 days	**Topic 13**	Sorting, Classifying, Counting, and Categorizing Data
8 days	**Topic 14**	Identifying and Describing Shapes
5 days	**Topic 15**	Position and Location of Shapes
5 days	**Topic 16**	Analyzing, Comparing, and Composing Shapes
10 days	**Step-Up**	Step-Up to Grade 1 Lessons
120 days		

Standards for Mathematical Content

Critical Area Representing, relating, and operating on whole numbers, initially with sets of objects

Domain Counting and Cardinality

Cluster Know number names and the count sequence.

Cluster Count to tell the number of objects.

Standards K.CC.3, K.CC.4, K.CC.4.a, K.CC.4.b, K.CC.5

Topic 1 One to Five

Standards for Mathematical Content

Critical Area Representing, relating, and operating on whole numbers, initially with sets of objects

Domain Counting and Cardinality

Cluster Know number names and the count sequence.

Cluster Count to tell the number of objects.

Cluster Compare numbers.

Standards K.CC.3, K.CC.4, K.CC.4.b, K.CC.4.c, K.CC.5, K.CC.6

Topic 2 Comparing and Ordering 0 to 5

Standards for Mathematical Content

Critical Area Representing, relating, and operating on whole numbers, initially with sets of objects

Domain Counting and Cardinality

Cluster Know number names and the count sequence.

Cluster Count to tell the number of objects.

Standards **K.CC.3, K.CC.4, K.CC.4.a, K.CC.4.b, K.CC.4.c, K.CC.5**

Topic 3 Six to Ten

Standards for Mathematical Content

Critical Area Representing, relating, and operating on whole numbers, initially with sets of objects

Domain Counting and Cardinality

Cluster Compare numbers.

Cluster Know number names and the count sequence.

Standards **K.CC.2, K.CC.4.c, K.CC.6, K.CC.7, K.OA.1**

Topic 4 Comparing and Ordering Numbers 0 to 10

Standards for Mathematical Content

Critical Area Representing, relating, and operating on whole numbers, initially with sets of objects

Domain Counting and Cardinality

Cluster Know number names and the count sequence.

Cluster Count to tell the number of objects.

Standards **K.CC.2, K.CC.3, K.CC.4.b**

Topic 5 Numbers to 20

Standards for Mathematical Content

Critical Area Representing, relating, and operating on whole numbers, initially with sets of objects

Domain Counting and Cardinality

Cluster Know number names and the count sequence.

Cluster Count to tell the number of objects.

Standards **K.CC.1, K.CC.2, K.CC.4.b, K.CC.4.c, K.CC.5**

Topic 6 Numbers to 100

Standards for Mathematical Content

Critical Area Representing, relating, and operating on whole numbers, initially with sets of objects

Domain Operations and Algebraic Thinking

Cluster Understand addition as putting together and adding to, and understand subtraction as taking apart and taking from.

Standards K.OA.1, K.OA.2, K.OA.5

Topic 7 Understanding Addition

Standards for Mathematical Content

Critical Area Representing, relating, and operating on whole numbers, initially with sets of objects

Domain Operations and Algebraic Thinking

Cluster Understand addition as putting together and adding to, and understand subtraction as taking apart and taking from.

Standards K.OA.1, K.OA.2, K.OA.5

Topic 8 Understanding Subtraction

Standards for Mathematical Content

Critical Area Representing, relating, and operating on whole numbers, initially with sets of objects

Domain Operations and Algebraic Thinking

Cluster Understand addition as putting together and adding to, and understand subtraction as taking apart and taking from.

Cluster Classify objects into given categories; count the numbers of objects in each category and sort the categories by count.

Standards K.OA.3, K.OA.4, K.MD.3

Topic 9 More Addition and Subtraction

Planning

Lessons

Review and Assessment

Standards for Mathematical Content

Critical Area Representing, relating, and operating on whole numbers, initially with sets of objects

Domain Number and Operations in Base Ten

Cluster Work with numbers 11–19 to gain foundations for place value.

Standard K.NBT.1

Topic 10 Composing Numbers 11 to 19

Standards for Mathematical Content

Critical Area Representing, relating, and operating on whole numbers, initially with sets of objects

Domain Number and Operations in Base Ten

Cluster Work with numbers 11–19 to gain foundations for place value.

Standard K.NBT.1

Topic 11 Decomposing Numbers 11 to 19

Standards for Mathematical Content

Critical Area Describing shapes and space

Domain Measurement and Data

Cluster Describe and compare measurable attributes.

Standards **K.MD.1, K.MD.2**

Topic 12 Measurement

Planning

Lessons

Review and Assessment

Standards for Mathematical Content

Critical Area Describing shapes and space

Domain Measurement and Data

Cluster Classify objects and count the number of objects in each category.

Standards K.MD.3, K.G.1

Topic 13 Sorting, Classifying, Counting, and Categorizing Data

Standards for Mathematical Content

Critical Area Describing shapes and space

Domain Geometry

Cluster Identify and describe shapes (squares, circles, triangles, rectangles, hexagons, cubes, cones, cylinders, and spheres).

Standards K.G.2, K.G.3

Topic 14 Identifying and Describing Shapes

Standards for Mathematical Content

Critical Area Describing shapes and space

Domain Geometry

Cluster Identify and describe shapes (squares, circles, triangles, rectangles, hexagons, cubes, cones, cylinders, and spheres).

Standard K.G.1

Topic 15 Position and Location of Shapes

Planning

Lessons

Review and Assessment

Standards for Mathematical Content

Critical Area Describing shapes and space

Domain Geometry

Cluster Identify and describe shapes (squares, circles, triangles, rectangles, hexagons, cubes, cones, cylinders, and spheres).

Cluster Analyze, compare, create, and compose shapes.

Standards K.G.2, K.G.3, K.G.4, K.G.5, K.G.6

Topic 16 Analyzing, Comparing, and Composing Shapes

Planning

Lessons

Assessment and Reteaching

1 Make sense of problems and persevere in solving them.

Mathematically proficient students start by explaining to themselves the meaning of a problem and looking for entry points to its solution. They analyze givens, constraints, relationships, and goals. They make conjectures about the form and meaning of the solution and plan a solution pathway rather than simply jumping into a solution attempt. They consider analogous problems, and try special cases and simpler forms of the original problem in order to gain insight into its solution. They monitor and evaluate their progress and change course if necessary. Older students might, depending on the context of the problem, transform algebraic expressions or change the viewing window on their graphing calculator to get the information they need. Mathematically proficient students can explain correspondences between equations, verbal descriptions, tables, and graphs or draw diagrams of important features and relationships, graph data, and search for regularity or trends. Younger students might rely on using concrete objects or pictures to help conceptualize and solve a problem. Mathematically proficient students check their answers to problems using a different method, and they continually ask themselves, "Does this make sense?" They can understand the approaches of others to solving complex problems and identify correspondences between different approaches.

enVisionMATH Common Core is built on a foundation of problem-based instruction that has sense-making at its heart. Each topic includes at least one problem-solving lesson in which students focus on honing their sense-making and problem-solving skills. Problem-solving lessons present to students a process that begins with making sense of the problem. *Read and Understand,* the first phase of the process, has students ask themselves, *What am I trying to find?* and *What do I know?,* questions that will help identify the givens and constraints of the problem. In the second phase, *Plan and Solve,* students decide on a solution plan. In the final phase, *Look Back and Check,* students verify that their work is reasonable and reflects the information given.

Each lesson begins with **Problem-Based Interactive Learning,** an activity in which students interact with their peers and teachers to make sense of and decide on a workable solution for a real-world situation. Another feature of each lesson is the set of problem-solving exercises in which students persevere by applying different skills and strategies to solve problems.

Found throughout the program; some examples:

Lesson 2-3	**Lesson 6-5**	**Lesson 10-2**	**Lesson 14-6**
Lesson 2-8	**Lesson 6-6**	**Lesson 10-4**	**Lesson 15-2**
Lesson 2-10	**Lesson 7-3**	**Lesson 11-3**	**Lesson 15-4**
Lesson 3-2	**Lesson 7-6**	**Lesson 11-5**	**Lesson 15-5**
Lesson 4-1	**Lesson 7-7**	**Lesson 12-1**	**Lesson 16-4**
Lesson 4-5	**Lesson 8-2**	**Lesson 12-3**	**Lesson 16-5**
Lesson 4-9	**Lesson 8-8**	**Lesson 13-3**	
Lesson 5-5	**Lesson 9-3**	**Lesson 13-4**	
Lesson 6-2	**Lesson 9-7**	**Lesson 13-5**	

2 Reason abstractly and quantitatively.

Mathematically proficient students make sense of quantities and their relationships in problem situations. They bring two complementary abilities to bear on problems involving quantitative relationships: the ability to *decontextualize*—to abstract a given situation and represent it symbolically and manipulate the representing symbols as if they have a life of their own, without necessarily attending to their referents—and the ability to *contextualize,* to pause as needed during the manipulation process in order to probe into the referents for the symbols involved. Quantitative reasoning entails habits of creating a coherent representation of the problem at hand; considering the units involved; attending to the meaning of quantities, not just how to compute them; and knowing and flexibly using different properties of operations and objects.

enVisionMATH Common Core provides scaffolded instruction to help students develop both quantitative and abstract reasoning. In the **Visual Learning Bridge,** students can see how to represent a given situation numerically or algebraically. They will have opportunities later in the lesson to reason abstractly as they endeavor to represent situations symbolically. Reasonableness exercises remind students to compare their work to the original situation. In the **Do You Understand?** part of the Guided Practice, students gain experiences with quantitative reasoning as they consider the meaning of different parts of an expression or equation. Reasoning problems throughout the exercise sets focus students' attention on the structure or meaning of an operation, for example, rather than merely the solution.

Found throughout the program; some examples:

Lesson 1-4	**Lesson 4-9**	**Lesson 7-7**	**Lesson 12-2**
Lesson 1-6	**Lesson 5-2**	**Lesson 9-2**	**Lesson 12-5**
Lesson 2-2	**Lesson 5-5**	**Lesson 9-4**	**Lesson 14-5**
Lesson 2-10	**Lesson 6-3**	**Lesson 9-9**	**Lesson 14-6**
Lesson 3-3	**Lesson 6-5**	**Lesson 10-1**	**Lesson 16-4**
Lesson 3-6	**Lesson 6-6**	**Lesson 10-3**	**Lesson 16-5**
Lesson 4-4	**Lesson 7-5**	**Lesson 11-2**	

"Convince Me!"

*3 Construct viable arguments and critique the reasoning of others.

Mathematically proficient students understand and use stated assumptions, definitions, and previously established results in constructing arguments. They make conjectures and build a logical progression of statements to explore the truth of their conjectures. They are able to analyze situations by breaking them into cases, and can recognize and use counterexamples. They justify their conclusions, communicate them to others, and respond to the arguments of others. They reason inductively about data, making plausible arguments that take into account the context from which the data arose. Mathematically proficient students are also able to compare the effectiveness of two plausible arguments, distinguish correct logic or reasoning from that which is flawed, and—if there is a flaw in an argument—explain what it is. Elementary students can construct arguments using concrete referents such as objects, drawings, diagrams, and actions. Such arguments can make sense and be correct, even though they are not generalized or made formal until later grades. Later, students learn to determine domains to which an argument applies. Students at all grades can listen or read the arguments of others, decide whether they make sense, and ask useful questions to clarify or improve the arguments.

Consistent with a focus on reasoning and sense-making is a focus on critical reasoning – argumentation and critique of arguments. In Pearson's *enVisionMATH Common Core,* the **Problem-Based Interactive Learning** affords students opportunities to share with classmates their thinking about problems, their solution methods, and their reasoning about the solutions. Many exercises found throughout the program specifically call for students to justify or explain their solutions. **Journal** activities help students develop foundational critical reasoning skills by having them construct explanations for processes. The ability to articulate a clear explanation for a process is a stepping stone to critical analysis and reasoning of both the student's own processes and those of others.

Found throughout the program; some examples:

Lesson 2-1	**Lesson 5-5**	**Lesson 9-4**	**Lesson 15-3**
Lesson 3-1	**Lesson 7-3**	**Lesson 11-3**	**Lesson 15-5**
Lesson 3-6	**Lesson 7-7**	**Lesson 12-4**	**Lesson 16-2**
Lesson 4-2	**Lesson 8-2**	**Lesson 12-8**	
Lesson 4-4	**Lesson 8-7**	**Lesson 14-2**	
Lesson 5-1	**Lesson 9-2**	**Lesson 14-3**	

4 Model with mathematics.

Mathematically proficient students can apply the mathematics they know to solve problems arising in everyday life, society, and the workplace. In early grades, this might be as simple as writing an addition equation to describe a situation. In middle grades, a student might apply proportional reasoning to plan a school event or analyze a problem in the community. By high school, a student might use geometry to solve a design problem or use a function to describe how one quantity of interest depends on another. Mathematically proficient students who can apply what they know are comfortable making assumptions and approximations to simplify a complicated situation, realizing that these may need revision later. They are able to identify important quantities in a practical situation and map their relationships using such tools as diagrams, two-way tables, graphs, flowcharts and formulas. They can analyze those relationships mathematically to draw conclusions. They routinely interpret their mathematical results in the context of the situation and reflect on whether the results make sense, possibly improving the model if it has not served its purpose.

Students in Pearson's *enVisionMATH Common Core* are introduced to mathematical modeling in the early grades. They first use manipulatives and drawings and then equations to model addition and subtraction situations. The **Visual Learning Bridge** and **Visual Learning Animation** often present real-world situations, and students are shown how these can be modeled mathematically. In later grades, students expand their modeling skills to include representations such as tables and graphs, as well as equations.

Found throughout the program; some examples:

Lesson 1-1	**Lesson 5-4**	**Lesson 9-5**	**Lesson 13-5**
Lesson 1-4	**Lesson 7-4**	**Lesson 9-9**	**Lesson 16-3**
Lesson 1-7	**Lesson 7-7**	**Lesson 10-2**	**Lesson 16-5**
Lesson 4-2	**Lesson 8-2**	**Lesson 11-1**	
Lesson 4-6	**Lesson 8-5**	**Lesson 11-4**	
Lesson 4-8	**Lesson 8-7**	**Lesson 12-1**	
Lesson 5-3	**Lesson 9-1**	**Lesson 13-3**	

5 Use appropriate tools strategically.

Mathematically proficient students consider the available tools when solving a mathematical problem. These tools might include pencil and paper, concrete models, a ruler, a protractor, a calculator, a spreadsheet, a computer algebra system, a statistical package, or dynamic geometry software. Proficient students are sufficiently familiar with tools appropriate for their grade or course to make sound decisions about when each of these tools might be helpful, recognizing both the insight to be gained and their limitations. For example, mathematically proficient high school students analyze graphs of functions and solutions generated using a graphing calculator. They detect possible errors by strategically using estimation and other mathematical knowledge. When making mathematical models, they know that technology can enable them to visualize the results of varying assumptions, explore consequences, and compare predictions with data. Mathematically proficient students at various grade levels are able to identify relevant external mathematical resources, such as digital content located on a website, and use them to pose or solve problems. They are able to use technological tools to explore and deepen their understanding of concepts.

Students become fluent in the use of a wide assortment of tools ranging from physical objects, including manipulatives, rulers, protractors, and even pencil and paper, to digital tools, such as eTools, calculators, and computers. As students become more familiar with the tools available to them, they are able to begin making decisions about which tools are most helpful in a particular situation.

Throughout the program; for examples, see:

Lesson 1-2	**Lesson 5-2**	**Lesson 10-1**	**Lesson 13-7**
Lesson 1-7	**Lesson 6-4**	**Lesson 11-1**	**Lesson 14-5**
Lesson 2-4	**Lesson 6-6**	**Lesson 11-2**	**Lesson 14-8**
Lesson 3-2	**Lesson 7-1**	**Lesson 11-4**	**Lesson 15-1**
Lesson 3-6	**Lesson 7-7**	**Lesson 12-4**	**Lesson 15-5**
Lesson 4-6	**Lesson 8-1**	**Lesson 12-7**	**Lesson 16-4**
Lesson 4-10	**Lesson 8-8**	**Lesson 12-8**	
Lesson 5-1	**Lesson 9-2**	**Lesson 13-4**	

* Understanding vocabulary (of what they're being asked)

6 Attend to precision.

Mathematically proficient students try to communicate precisely to others. They try to use clear definitions in discussion with others and in their own reasoning. They state the meaning of the symbols they choose, including using the equal sign consistently and appropriately. They are careful about specifying units of measure, and labeling axes to clarify the correspondence with quantities in a problem. They calculate accurately and efficiently, express numerical answers with a degree of precision appropriate for the problem context. In the elementary grades, students give carefully formulated explanations to each other. By the time they reach high school they have learned to examine claims and make explicit use of definitions.

Students are expected to use mathematical terms and symbols with precision. Key terms and concepts are highlighted in each lesson. The **Problem-Based Interactive Learning** activity provides repeated opportunities for children to use precise language to explain their solution paths while solving problems. In the **Do You Understand?** feature, students revisit these key terms or concepts and provide explicit definitions or explanations.

Throughout the program; for examples, see:

Lesson 1-2	**Lesson 5-4**	**Lesson 9-9**	**Lesson 14-4**
Lesson 1-7	**Lesson 5-5**	**Lesson 10-2**	**Lesson 15-2**
Lesson 2-5	**Lesson 7-3**	**Lesson 11-1**	**Lesson 15-4**
Lesson 2-8	**Lesson 7-6**	**Lesson 11-3**	**Lesson 15-5**
Lesson 3-6	**Lesson 8-1**	**Lesson 13-1**	**Lesson 16-1**
Lesson 4-2	**Lesson 8-6**	**Lesson 13-7**	
Lesson 4-9	**Lesson 9-3**	**Lesson 14-1**	

7 Look for and make use of structure.

Mathematically proficient students look closely to discern a pattern or structure. Young students, for example, might notice that three and seven more is the same amount as seven and three more, or they may sort a collection of shapes according to how many sides the shapes have. Later, students will see 7×8 equals the well-remembered $7 \times 5 + 7 \times 3$, in preparation for learning about the distributive property. In the expression $x^2 + 9x + 14$, older students can see the 14 as 2×7 and the 9 as $2 + 7$. They recognize the significance of an existing line in a geometric figure and can use the strategy of drawing an auxiliary line for solving problems. They also can step back for an overview and shift perspective. They can see complicated things, such as some algebraic expressions, as single objects or as being composed of several objects. For example, they can see $5 - 3(x + y)^2$ as 5 minus a positive number times a square and use that to realize that its value cannot be more than 5 for any real numbers x and y.

Students are encouraged to look for structure as they develop solution plans. In the **Look for a Pattern** problem-solving lessons, children in the early years develop a sense of patterning with visual and physical objects. As students mature in their mathematical thinking, they look for structure in numerical operations by focusing on place value and properties of operations. This focus on looking for and recognizing structure enables students to draw from patterns as they formalize their thinking about the structure of operations.

Throughout the program; for examples, see:

Lesson 1-1	**Lesson 5-5**	**Lesson 10-4**	**Lesson 14-2**
Lesson 1-5	**Lesson 6-1**	**Lesson 11-5**	**Lesson 14-7**
Lesson 3-7	**Lesson 6-6**	**Lesson 12-1**	**Lesson 15-5**
Lesson 4-1	**Lesson 7-4**	**Lesson 12-7**	**Lesson 16-1**
Lesson 4-6	**Lesson 9-9**	**Lesson 13-2**	**Lesson 16-3**
Lesson 4-10	**Lesson 10-2**	**Lesson 13-5**	

8 Look for and express regularity in repeated reasoning.

Mathematically proficient students notice if calculations are repeated, and look both for general methods and for shortcuts. Upper elementary students might notice when dividing 25 by 11 that they are repeating the same calculations over and over again, and conclude they have a repeating decimal. By paying attention to the calculation of slope as they repeatedly check whether points are on the line through (1, 2) with slope 3, middle school students might abstract the equation $(y - 2)/(x - 1) = 3$. Noticing the regularity in the way terms cancel when expanding $(x - 1)(x + 1)$, $(x - 1)(x^2 + x + 1)$, and $(x - 1)(x^3 + x^2 + x + 1)$ might lead them to the general formula for the sum of a geometric series. As they work to solve a problem, mathematically proficient students maintain oversight of the process, while attending to the details. They continually evaluate the reasonableness of their intermediate results.

Students are prompted to look for repetition in computations to help them develop shortcuts and become more efficient problem-solvers. Students are reminded to think about problems they have encountered previously that may share features or processes. They are encouraged to draw on the solution plan developed for such problems, and as their mathematical thinking matures, to look for and apply generalizations to similar situations. The **Problem-Based Interactive Learning** activities offer students opportunities to look for regularity in the way operations behave.

Throughout the program; for examples, see:

Lesson 1-7	**Lesson 3-8**	**Lesson 7-3**	**Lesson 14-8**
Lesson 2-3	**Lesson 4-2**	**Lesson 7-7**	**Lesson 15-5**
Lesson 2-7	**Lesson 4-6**	**Lesson 10-3**	**Lesson 16-5**
Lesson 2-9	**Lesson 4-7**	**Lesson 11-5**	
Lesson 3-1	**Lesson 5-1**	**Lesson 12-2**	
Lesson 3-4	**Lesson 5-5**	**Lesson 12-8**	

DOMAIN K.CC Counting and Cardinality

Know number names and the count sequence.

Common Core State Standard	Student's Edition Pages	Teacher's Edition Pages*
K.CC.1 Count to 100 by ones and by tens.	**109–110,** Lesson 6-1 **113–114,** Lesson 6-3 **115–116,** Lesson 6-4 **117–118,** Lesson 6-5 **119–120,** Lesson 6-6 **121–122,** Reteaching Sets B–D	**109A–110C,** Lesson 6-1 **113A–114C,** Lesson 6-3 **115A–116C,** Lesson 6-4 **117A–118C,** Lesson 6-5 **119A–120C,** Lesson 6-6 **121–122,** Reteaching Sets B–D
K.CC.2 Count forward beginning from a given number within the known sequence (instead of having to begin at 1).	**81–82,** Lesson 4-8 **83–84,** Lesson 4-9 **88,** Reteaching Set C **101–102,** Lesson 5-5 **104,** Reteaching Set C **109–110,** Lesson 6-1 **113–114,** Lesson 6-3 **119–120,** Lesson 6-6 **122,** Reteaching Set C	**81A–82C,** Lesson 4-8 **83A–84C,** Lesson 4-9 **88,** Reteaching Set C **101A–102C,** Lesson 5-5 **104,** Reteaching Set C **109A–110C,** Lesson 6-1 **113A–114C,** Lesson 6-3 **119A–120C,** Lesson 6-6 **122,** Reteaching Set C
K.CC.3 Write numbers from 0 to 20. Represent a number of objects with a written numeral 0–20 (with 0 representing a count of no objects).	**7–8,** Lesson 1-3 **13–14,** Lesson 1-6 **17,** Reteaching Sets A, B **29–30,** Lesson 2-4 **31–32,** Lesson 2-5 **42,** Reteaching Set C **49–50,** Lesson 3-2 **53–54,** Lesson 3-4 **57–58,** Lesson 3-6 **61,** Reteaching Set A **93–94,** Lesson 5-1 **95–96,** Lesson 5-2 **97–98,** Lesson 5-3 **99–100,** Lesson 5-4 **103,** Reteaching Sets A, B	**7A–8C,** Lesson 1-3 **13A–14C,** Lesson 1-6 **17,** Reteaching Sets A, B **29A–30C,** Lesson 2-4 **31A–32C,** Lesson 2-5 **42,** Reteaching Set C **49A–50C,** Lesson 3-2 **53A–54C,** Lesson 3-4 **57A–58C,** Lesson 3-6 **61,** Reteaching Set A **93A–94C,** Lesson 5-1 **95A–96C,** Lesson 5-2 **97A–98C,** Lesson 5-3 **99A–100C,** Lesson 5-4 **103,** Reteaching Sets A, B

***Teacher's Resource Masters** for every lesson (Practice, Reteaching, Enrichment, Centers, Quick Check) are considered part of this correlation.

DOMAIN K.CC Counting and Cardinality *cont.*

Count to tell the number of objects.

Common Core State Standard	Student's Edition Pages	Teacher's Edition Pages*
K.CC.4 Understand the relationship between numbers and quantities; connect counting to cardinality.	**7–8,** Lesson 1-3 **13–14,** Lesson 1-6 **17–18,** Reteaching Sets A–C **31–32,** Lesson 2-5 **37–38,** Lesson 2-8 **42,** Reteaching Set D **49–50,** Lesson 3-2 **53–54,** Lesson 3-4 **57–58,** Lesson 3-6 **61–62,** Reteaching Sets A–D	**7A–8C,** Lesson 1-3 **13A–14C,** Lesson 1-6 **17–18,** Reteaching Sets A–C **31A–32C,** Lesson 2-5 **37A–38C,** Lesson 2-8 **42,** Reteaching Set D **49A–50C,** Lesson 3-2 **53A–54C,** Lesson 3-4 **57A–58C,** Lesson 3-6 **61–62,** Reteaching Sets A–D
K.CC.4.a When counting objects, say the number names in the standard order, pairing each object with one and only one number name and each number name with one and only one object.	**3–4,** Lesson 1-1 **9–10,** Lesson 1-4 **17–18,** Reteaching Sets A–C **37–38,** Lesson 2-5 **41–42,** Reteaching Sets A–C **59–60,** Lesson 3-7 **61–62,** Reteaching Sets A–D	**3A–4C,** Lesson 1-1 **9A–10C,** Lesson 1-4 **17–18,** Reteaching Sets A–C **37A–38C,** Lesson 2-5 **41–42,** Reteaching Sets A–C **59A–60C,** Lesson 3-7 **61–62,** Reteaching Sets A–D
K.CC.4.b Understand that the last number name said tells the number of objects counted. The number of objects is the same regardless of their arrangement or the order in which they were counted.	**5–6,** Lesson 1-2 **11–12,** Lesson 1-5 **15–16,** Lesson 1-7 **18,** Reteaching Set C **39–40,** Lesson 2-9 **42,** Reteaching Set C **47–48,** Lesson 3-1 **51–52,** Lesson 3-3 **55–56,** Lesson 3-5 **59–60,** Lesson 3-7 **61–62,** Reteaching Sets B, D **93–94,** Lesson 5-1 **95–96,** Lesson 5-2 **97–98,** Lesson 5-3 **99–100,** Lesson 5-4 **103,** Reteaching Sets A, B **109–110,** Lesson 6-1 **121–122,** Reteaching Sets B, C	**5A–6C,** Lesson 1-2 **11A–12C,** Lesson 1-5 **15A–16C,** Lesson 1-7 **18,** Reteaching Set C **39A–40C,** Lesson 2-9 **42,** Reteaching Set C **47A–48C,** Lesson 3-1 **51A–52C,** Lesson 3-3 **55A–56C,** Lesson 3-5 **59A–60C,** Lesson 3-7 **61–62,** Reteaching Sets B, D **93A–94C,** Lesson 5-1 **95A–96C,** Lesson 5-2 **97A–98C,** Lesson 5-3 **99A–100C,** Lesson 5-4 **103,** Reteaching Sets A, B **109A–110C,** Lesson 6-1 **121–122,** Reteaching Sets B, C
K.CC.4.c Understand that each successive number name refers to a quantity that is one larger.	**35–36,** Lesson 2-7 **37–38,** Lesson 2-8 **39–40,** Lesson 2-9 **42,** Reteaching Set C **59–60,** Lesson 3-7 **61–62,** Reteaching Sets A–D **81–82,** Lesson 4-8 **87,** Reteaching Sets A, B **113–114,** Lesson 6-3 **121–122,** Reteaching Sets B, C	**35A–36C,** Lesson 2-7 **37A–38C,** Lesson 2-8 **39A–40A,** Lesson 2-9 **42,** Reteaching Set C **59A–60C,** Lesson 3-7 **61–62,** Reteaching Sets A–D **81A–82C,** Lesson 4-8 **87,** Reteaching Sets A, B **113A–114C,** Lesson 6-3 **121–122,** Reteaching Sets B, C

***Teacher's Resource Masters** for every lesson (Practice, Reteaching, Enrichment, Centers, Quick Check) are considered part of this correlation.

DOMAIN K.CC **Counting and Cardinality** *cont.*

Common Core State Standard	**Student's Edition Pages**	**Teacher's Edition Pages***
K.CC.5 Count to answer "how many?" questions about as many as 20 things arranged in a line, a rectangular array, or a circle, or as many as 10 things in a scattered configuration; given a number from 1–20, count out that many objects.	**3–4,** Lesson 1-1 **5–6,** Lesson 1-2 **7–8,** Lesson 1-3 **9–10,** Lesson 1-4 **11–12,** Lesson 1-5 **13–14,** Lesson 1-6 **15–16,** Lesson 1-7 **17–18,** Reteaching Sets A–C **31–32,** Lesson 2-5 **41–42,** Reteaching Sets B, C **47–48,** Lesson 3-1 **49–50,** Lesson 3-2 **51–52,** Lesson 3-3 **53–54,** Lesson 3-4 **55–56,** Lesson 3-5 **57–58,** Lesson 3-6 **61–62,** Reteaching Sets A–D **111–112,** Lesson 6-2 **121,** Reteaching Set A	**3A–4C,** Lesson 1-1 **5A–6C,** Lesson 1-2 **7A–8C,** Lesson 1-3 **9A–10C,** Lesson 1-4 **11A–12C,** Lesson 1-5 **13A–14C,** Lesson 1-6 **15A–16C,** Lesson 1-7 **17–18,** Reteaching Sets A–C **31A–32C,** Lesson 2-5 **41–42,** Reteaching Sets B, C **47A–48C,** Lesson 3-1 **49A–50C,** Lesson 3-2 **51A–52C,** Lesson 3-3 **53A–54C,** Lesson 3-4 **55A–56C,** Lesson 3-5 **57A–58C,** Lesson 3-6 **61–62,** Reteaching Sets A–D **111A–112C,** Lesson 6-2 **121,** Reteaching Set A

***Teacher's Resource Masters** for every lesson (Practice, Reteaching, Enrichment, Centers, Quick Check) are considered part of this correlation.

DOMAIN K.CC **Counting and Cardinality** *cont.*

Compare numbers.

Common Core State Standard	**Student's Edition Pages**	**Teacher's Edition Pages***
K.CC.6 Identify whether the number of objects in one group is greater than, less than, or equal to the number of objects in another group, e.g., by using matching and counting strategies.[1]	**23–24,** Lesson 2-1 **25–26,** Lesson 2-2 **27–28,** Lesson 2-3 **33–34,** Lesson 2-6 **39–40,** Lesson 2-9 **41,** Reteaching Sets A, B **67–68,** Lesson 4-1 **69–70,** Lesson 4-2 **71–72,** Lesson 4-3 **73–74,** Lesson 4-4 **75–76,** Lesson 4-5 **77–78,** Lesson 4-6 **79–80,** Lesson 4-7 **87,** Reteaching Sets A, B	**23A–24C,** Lesson 2-1 **25A–26C,** Lesson 2-2 **27A–28C,** Lesson 2-3 **33A–34C,** Lesson 2-6 **39A–40C,** Lesson 2-9 **41,** Reteaching Sets A, B **67A–68C,** Lesson 4-1 **69A–70C,** Lesson 4-2 **71A–72C,** Lesson 4-3 **73A–74C,** Lesson 4-4 **75A–76C,** Lesson 4-5 **77A–78C,** Lesson 4-6 **79A–80C,** Lesson 4-7 **87,** Reteaching Sets A, B
K.CC.7 Compare two numbers between 1 and 10 presented as written numerals.	**67–68,** Lesson 4-1 **69–70,** Lesson 4-2 **71–72,** Lesson 4-3 **73–74,** Lesson 4-4 **75–76,** Lesson 4-5 **77–78,** Lesson 4-6 **79–80,** Lesson 4-7 **85–86,** Lesson 4-10 **87,** Reteaching Set B	**67A–68C,** Lesson 4-1 **69A–70C,** Lesson 4-2 **71A–72C,** Lesson 4-3 **73A–74C,** Lesson 4-4 **75A–76C,** Lesson 4-5 **77A–78C,** Lesson 4-6 **79A–80C,** Lesson 4-7 **85A–86C,** Lesson 4-10 **87,** Reteaching Set B

***Teacher's Resource Masters** for every lesson (Practice, Reteaching, Enrichment, Centers, Quick Check) are considered part of this correlation.

DOMAIN K.OA Operations and Algebraic Thinking

Understand addition as putting together and adding to, and understand subtraction as taking apart and taking from.

Common Core State Standard	Student's Edition Pages	Teacher's Edition Pages*
K.OA.1 Represent addition and subtraction with objects, fingers, mental images, drawings[2], sounds (e.g., claps), acting out situations, verbal explanations, expressions, or equations.	**73–74,** Lesson 4-4 **75–76,** Lesson 4-5 **77–78,** Lesson 4-6 **79–80,** Lesson 4-7 **87,** Reteaching Set B **127–128,** Lesson 7-1 **129–130,** Lesson 7-2 **131–132,** Lesson 7-3 **133–134,** Lesson 7-4 **135–136,** Lesson 7-5 **137–138,** Lesson 7-6 **139–140,** Lesson 7-7 **141–142,** Reteaching Sets A–C **147–148,** Lesson 8-1 **149–150,** Lesson 8-2 **151–152,** Lesson 8-3 **153–154,** Lesson 8-4 **155–156,** Lesson 8-5 **157–158,** Lesson 8-6 **159–160,** Lesson 8-7 **161–162,** Lesson 8-8 **163–164,** Reteaching Sets A–D **185–186,** Lesson 9-9	**73A–74C,** Lesson 4-4 **75A–76C,** Lesson 4-5 **77A–78C,** Lesson 4-6 **79A–80C,** Lesson 4-7 **87,** Reteaching Set B **127A–128C,** Lesson 7-1 **129A–130C,** Lesson 7-2 **131A–132C,** Lesson 7-3 **133A–134C,** Lesson 7-4 **135A–136C,** Lesson 7-5 **137A–138C,** Lesson 7-6 **139A–140C,** Lesson 7-7 **141–142,** Reteaching Sets A–C **147A–148C,** Lesson 8-1 **149A–150C,** Lesson 8-2 **151A–152C,** Lesson 8-3 **153A–154C,** Lesson 8-4 **155A–156C,** Lesson 8-5 **157A–158C,** Lesson 8-6 **159A–160C,** Lesson 8-7 **161A–162C,** Lesson 8-8 **163–164,** Reteaching Sets A–D **185A–186C,** Lesson 9-9
K.OA.2 Solve addition and subtraction word problems, and add and subtract within 10, e.g., by using objects or drawings to represent the problem.	**127–128,** Lesson 7-1 **129–130,** Lesson 7-2 **131–132,** Lesson 7-3 **133–134,** Lesson 7-4 **135–136,** Lesson 7-5 **137–138,** Lesson 7-6 **139–140,** Lesson 7-7 **141,** Reteaching Sets A, B **147–148,** Lesson 8-1 **149–150,** Lesson 8-2 **151–152,** Lesson 8-3 **153–154,** Lesson 8-4 **155–156,** Lesson 8-5 **157–158,** Lesson 8-6 **159–160,** Lesson 8-7 **161–162,** Lesson 8-8 **163–164,** Reteaching Sets A-D	**127A–128C,** Lesson 7-1 **129A–130C,** Lesson 7-2 **131A–132C,** Lesson 7-3 **133A–134C,** Lesson 7-4 **135A–136C,** Lesson 7-5 **137A–138C,** Lesson 7-6 **139A–140C,** Lesson 7-7 **141,** Reteaching Sets A, B **147A–148C,** Lesson 8-1 **149A–150C,** Lesson 8-2 **151A–152C,** Lesson 8-3 **153A–154C,** Lesson 8-4 **155A–156C,** Lesson 8-5 **157A–158C,** Lesson 8-6 **159A–160C,** Lesson 8-7 **161A–162C,** Lesson 8-8 **163–164,** Reteaching Sets A-D

***Teacher's Resource Masters** for every lesson (Practice, Reteaching, Enrichment, Centers, Quick Check) are considered part of this correlation.

DOMAIN K.OA Operations and Algebraic Thinking *cont.*

Common Core State Standard	Student's Edition Pages	Teacher's Edition Pages*
K.OA.3 Decompose numbers less than or equal to 10 into pairs in more than one way, e.g., by using objects or drawings, and record each decomposition by a drawing or equation (e.g., 5 = 2 + 3 and 5 = 4 + 1).	**169–170,** Lesson 9-1 **171–172,** Lesson 9-2 **173–174,** Lesson 9-3 **175–176,** Lesson 9-4 **177–178,** Lesson 9-5 **179–180,** Lesson 9-6 **183–184,** Lesson 9-8 **187–188,** Reteaching Sets A, C, D	**169A–170C,** Lesson 9-1 **171A–172C,** Lesson 9-2 **173A–174C,** Lesson 9-3 **175A–176C,** Lesson 9-4 **177A–178C,** Lesson 9-5 **179A–180C,** Lesson 9-6 **183A–184C,** Lesson 9-8 **187–188,** Reteaching Sets A, C, D
K.OA.4 For any number from 1 to 9, find the number that makes 10 when added to the given number, e.g., by using objects or drawings, and record the answer with a drawing or equation.	**181–182,** Lesson 9-7 **187,** Reteaching Set B	**181A–182C,** Lesson 9-7 **187,** Reteaching Set B
K.OA.5 Fluently add and subtract within 5.	**127–128,** Lesson 7-1 **129–130,** Lesson 7-2 **131–132,** Lesson 7-3 **133–134,** Lesson 7-4 **135–136,** Lesson 7-5 **137–138,** Lesson 7-6 **139–140,** Lesson 7-7 **141,** Reteaching Sets A, B **147–148,** Lesson 8-1 **149–150,** Lesson 8-2 **151–152,** Lesson 8-3 **153–154,** Lesson 8-4 **155–156,** Lesson 8-5 **157–158,** Lesson 8-6 **159–160,** Lesson 8-7 **163–164,** Reteaching Sets A–D	**127A–128C,** Lesson 7-1 **129A–130C,** Lesson 7-2 **131A–132C,** Lesson 7-3 **133A–134C,** Lesson 7-4 **135A–136C,** Lesson 7-5 **137A–138C,** Lesson 7-6 **139A–140C,** Lesson 7-7 **141,** Reteaching Sets A, B **147A–148C,** Lesson 8-1 **149A–150C,** Lesson 8-2 **151A–152C,** Lesson 8-3 **153A–154C,** Lesson 8-4 **155A–156C,** Lesson 8-5 **157A–158C,** Lesson 8-6 **159A–160C,** Lesson 8-7 **163–164,** Reteaching Sets A–D

***Teacher's Resource Masters** for every lesson (Practice, Reteaching, Enrichment, Centers, Quick Check) are considered part of this correlation.

DOMAIN K.NBT Number and Operations in Base Ten

Work with numbers 11–19 to gain foundations for place value.

Common Core State Standard	Student's Edition Pages	Teacher's Edition Pages*
K.NBT.1 Compose and decompose numbers from 11 to 19 into ten ones and some further ones, e.g., by using objects or drawings, and record each composition or decomposition by a drawing or equation (e.g., 18 = 10 + 8); understand that these numbers are composed of ten ones and one, two, three, four, five, six, seven, eight, or nine ones.	**193–194,** Lesson 10-1 **195–196,** Lesson 10-2 **197–198,** Lesson 10-3 **199–200,** Lesson 10-4 **201–202,** Reteaching Sets A–D **207–208,** Lesson 11-1 **209–210,** Lesson 11-2 **211–212,** Lesson 11-3 **213–214,** Lesson 11-4 **215–216,** Lesson 11-5 **217–218,** Reteaching Sets A–D	**193A–194C,** Lesson 10-1 **195A–196C,** Lesson 10-2 **197A–198C,** Lesson 10-3 **199A–200C,** Lesson 10-4 **201–202,** Reteaching Sets A–D **207A–208C,** Lesson 11-1 **209A–210C,** Lesson 11-2 **211A–212C,** Lesson 11-3 **213A–214C,** Lesson 11-4 **215A–216C,** Lesson 11-5 **217–218,** Reteaching Sets A–D

***Teacher's Resource Masters** for every lesson (Practice, Reteaching, Enrichment, Centers, Quick Check) are considered part of this correlation.

DOMAIN K.MD Measurement and Data

Common Core State Standard	Student's Edition Pages	Teacher's Edition Pages*
Describe and compare measurable attributes.		
K.MD.1 Describe measurable attributes of objects, such as length or weight. Describe several measurable attributes of a single object.	**223–224,** Lesson 12-1 **225–226,** Lesson 12-2 **227–228,** Lesson 12-3 **229–230,** Lesson 12-4 **231–232,** Lesson 12-5 **233–234,** Lesson 12-6 **235–236,** Lesson 12-7 **237–238,** Lesson 12-8 **240,** Reteaching Set D	**223A–224C,** Lesson 12-1 **225A–226C,** Lesson 12-2 **227A–228C,** Lesson 12-3 **229A–230C,** Lesson 12-4 **231A–232C,** Lesson 12-5 **233A–234C,** Lesson 12-6 **235A–236C,** Lesson 12-7 **237A–238C,** Lesson 12-8 **240,** Reteaching Set D
K.MD.2 Directly compare two objects with a measurable attribute in common, to see which object has "more of"/"less of" the attribute, and describe the difference. *For example, directly compare the heights of two children and describe one child as taller/shorter.*	**225–226,** Lesson 12-2 **227–228,** Lesson 12-3 **229–230,** Lesson 12-4 **231–232,** Lesson 12-5 **233–234,** Lesson 12-6 **235–236,** Lesson 12-7 **237–238,** Lesson 12-8 **239–240,** Reteaching Sets A–C	**225A–226C,** Lesson 12-2 **227A–228C,** Lesson 12-3 **229A–230C,** Lesson 12-4 **231A–232C,** Lesson 12-5 **233A–234C,** Lesson 12-6 **235A–236C,** Lesson 12-7 **237A–238C,** Lesson 12-8 **239–240,** Reteaching Sets A–C
Classify objects and count the number of objects in each category.		
K.MD.3 Classify objects into given categories; count the numbers of objects in each category and sort the categories by count.[3]	**185–186,** Lesson 9-9 **245–246,** Lesson 13-1 **247–248,** Lesson 13-2 **249–250,** Lesson 13-3 **251–252,** Lesson 13-4 **253–254,** Lesson 13-5 **255–256,** Lesson 13-6 **257–258,** Lesson 13-7 **259–260,** Reteaching Sets A–D	**185A–186C,** Lesson 9-9 **245A–246C,** Lesson 13-1 **247A–248C,** Lesson 13-2 **249A–250C,** Lesson 13-3 **251A–252C,** Lesson 13-4 **253A–254C,** Lesson 13-5 **255A–256C,** Lesson 13-6 **257A–258C,** Lesson 13-7 **259–260,** Reteaching Sets A–D

***Teacher's Resource Masters** for every lesson (Practice, Reteaching, Enrichment, Centers, Quick Check) are considered part of this correlation.

DOMAIN K.G Geometry

Identify and describe shapes (squares, circles, triangles, rectangles, hexagons, cubes, cones, cylinders, and spheres).

Common Core State Standard	Student's Edition Pages	Teacher's Edition Pages*
K.G.1 Describe objects in the environment using names of shapes, and describe the relative positions of these objects using terms such as *above, below, beside, in front of, behind,* and *next to.*	**253–254,** Lesson 13-5 **260,** Reteaching Set C **287–288,** Lesson 15-1 **289–290,** Lesson 15-2 **291–292,** Lesson 15-3 **293–294,** Lesson 15-4 **295–296,** Lesson 15-5 **297–298,** Reteaching Sets A–D	**253A–254C,** Lesson 13-5 **260,** Reteaching Set C **287A–288C,** Lesson 15-1 **289A–290C,** Lesson 15-2 **291A–292C,** Lesson 15-3 **293A–294C,** Lesson 15-4 **295A–296C,** Lesson 15-5 **297–298,** Reteaching Sets A–D
K.G.2 Correctly name shapes regardless of their orientations or overall size.	**265–266,** Lesson 14-1 **267–268,** Lesson 14-2 **269–270,** Lesson 14-3 **271–272,** Lesson 14-4 **273–274,** Lesson 14-5 **275–276,** Lesson 14-6 **277–278,** Lesson 14-7 **279–280,** Lesson 14-8 **281,** Reteaching Sets A, B **303–304,** Lesson 16-1 **307–308,** Lesson 16-3 **309–310,** Lesson 16-4 **313,** Reteaching Sets A, B	**265A–266C,** Lesson 14-1 **267A–268C,** Lesson 14-2 **269A–270C,** Lesson 14-3 **271A–272C,** Lesson 14-4 **273A–274C,** Lesson 14-5 **275A–276C,** Lesson 14-6 **277A–278C,** Lesson 14-7 **279A–280C,** Lesson 14-8 **281,** Reteaching Sets A, B **303A–304C,** Lesson 16-1 **307A–308C,** Lesson 16-3 **309A–310C,** Lesson 16-4 **313,** Reteaching Sets A, B
K.G.3 Identify shapes as two-dimensional (lying in a plane, "flat") or three-dimensional ("solid").	**275–276,** Lesson 14-6 **277–278,** Lesson 14-7 **282,** Reteaching Set C **311–312,** Lesson 16-5 **313–314,** Reteaching Sets A–C	**275A–276C,** Lesson 14-6 **277A–278C,** Lesson 14-7 **282,** Reteaching Set C **311A–312C,** Lesson 16-5 **313–314,** Reteaching Sets A–C

***Teacher's Resource Masters** for every lesson (Practice, Reteaching, Enrichment, Centers, Quick Check) are considered part of this correlation.

DOMAIN K.G **Geometry** *cont.*

Analyze, compare, create, and compose shapes.

Common Core State Standard	Student's Edition Pages	Teacher's Edition Pages*
K.G.4 Analyze and compare two- and three-dimensional shapes, in different sizes and orientations, using informal language to describe their similarities, differences, parts (e.g., number of sides and vertices/"corners") and other attributes (e.g., having sides of equal length).	**303–304,** Lesson 16-1 **305–306,** Lesson 16-2 **307–308,** Lesson 16-3 **311–312,** Lesson 16-5 **313–314,** Reteaching Sets A–D	**303A–304C,** Lesson 16-1 **305A–306C,** Lesson 16-2 **307A–308C,** Lesson 16-3 **311A–312C,** Lesson 16-5 **313–314,** Reteaching Sets A–D
K.G.5 Model shapes in the world by building shapes from components (e.g., sticks and clay balls) and drawing shapes.	**309–310,** Lesson 16-4 **314,** Reteaching Set D	**309A–310C,** Lesson 16-4 **314,** Reteaching Set D
K.G.6 Compose simple shapes to form larger shapes. *For example, "Can you join these two triangles with full sides touching to make a rectangle?"*	**305–306,** Lesson 16-2 **314,** Reteaching Sets C, D	**305A–306C,** Lesson 16-2 **314,** Reteaching Sets C, D

***Teacher's Resource Masters** for every lesson (Practice, Reteaching, Enrichment, Centers, Quick Check) are considered part of this correlation.

Notes

1. Include groups with up to ten objects.
2. Drawings need not show details, but should show the mathematics in the problem. (This applies wherever drawings are mentioned in the Standards.)
3. Limit category counts to be less than or equal to 10.

Common Core

Standards for Mathematical Practice

Throughout the program, students at every grade level

- ✔ Make sense of problems and persevere in solving them.
- ✔ Reason abstractly and quantitatively.
- ✔ Construct viable arguments and critique the reasoning of others.
- ✔ Model with mathematics.
- ✔ Use appropriate tools strategically.
- ✔ Attend to precision.
- ✔ Look for and make use of structure.
- ✔ Look for and express regularity in repeated reasoning.

Common Core Domains

Domain Counting and Cardinality

	K	1	2	3	4	5	6
Know number names and the count sequence.							
Count to 100 by ones.	**K.CC.1** Topic 6						
Count to 100 by tens.	**K.CC.1** Topic 6						
Count forward from a given number.	**K.CC.2** Topics 4–6						
Write numbers from 0 to 20.	**K.CC.3** Topics 1–3, 5						
Represent up to 20 objects with a written numeral.	**K.CC.3** Topics 1–3, 5						
Count to tell the number of objects.							
Understand the relationship between numbers and quantities.	**K.CC.4** Topics 1–3						
Connect counting to cardinality.	**K.CC.4** Topics 1–3						
Count objects, saying the number names in the standard order.	**K.CC.4.a** Topics 1, 3						
Pair each object counted with one and only one number name and vice versa.	**K.CC.4.a** Topics 1, 3						
Connect the last number name said to the number of objects counted.	**K.CC.4.b** Topics 1–3, 5, 6						
Understand that the number of objects is the same regardless of how they were counted.	**K.CC.4.b** Topics 1, 5						
Understand that each successive number name represents one more.	**K.CC.4.c** Topics 2–4, 6						
Count up to 10 things in a scattered configuration.	**K.CC.5** Topics 1, 6						
Count up to 20 things in a line, rectangular array, or circle.	**K.CC.5** Topics 1, 6						
Count out up to 20 objects.	**K.CC.5** Topics 1–3, 6						
Compare numbers.							
Compare the number of objects in two groups.	**K.CC.6** Topics 2, 4						
Compare two numbers between 1 and 10.	**K.CC.7** Topic 4						

Domain **Operations and Algebraic Thinking**

	K	1	2	3	4	5	6
Understand addition as putting together and adding to, and understand subtraction as taking apart and taking from.							
Represent addition using a variety of models.	**K.OA.1** Topics 4, 7						
Represent subtraction using a variety of models.	**K.OA.1** Topics 4, 8						
Add within 10 using objects and drawings.	**K.OA.2** Topic 7						
Solve addition word problems within 10.	**K.OA.2** Topic 7						
Subtract within 10 using objects and drawings.	**K.OA.2** Topic 8						
Solve subtraction word problems within 10.	**K.OA.2** Topic 8						
Decompose numbers less than or equal to 10.	**K.OA.3** Topic 9						
Record decomposition of numbers less than or equal to 10.	**K.OA.3** Topic 9						
Make 10 using objects and drawings.	**K.OA.4** Topic 9						
Record how to make 10 using a drawing or equation.	**K.OA.4** Topic 9						
Fluently add within 5.	**K.OA.5** Topic 7						
Fluently subtract within 5.	**K.OA.5** Topic 8						
Represent and solve problems involving addition and subtraction.							
Add within 20 to solve word problems.		**1.OA.1** Topics 1, 4, 5					
Subtract within 20 to solve word problems.		**1.OA.1** Topics 2, 4, 6					
Solve word problems within 20 with three addends.		**1.OA.2** Topic 5					
Add within 100 to solve one-step word problems.			**2.OA.1** Topics 1–9				
Add within 100 to solve two-step word problems.			**2.OA.1** Topics 3, 9				
Subtract within 100 to solve one-step word problems.			**2.OA.1** Topics 1–9				
Subtract within 100 to solve two-step word problems.			**2.OA.1** Topics 3, 9				
Understand and apply properties of operations and the relationship between addition and subtraction.							
Apply properties of operations as strategies to add.		**1.OA.3** Topics 1, 4, 5					
Apply properties of operations as strategies to subtract.		**1.OA.3** Topics 2, 4, 6					
Understand subtraction as an unknown-addend problem.		**1.OA.4** Topics 2–4, 6					
Add and subtract within 20.							
Relate counting to addition.		**1.OA.5** Topics 3, 4					
Relate counting to subtraction.		**1.OA.5** Topics 3, 4					
Add within 20.		**1.OA.6** Topics 1, 4, 5					
Subtract within 20.		**1.OA.6** Topics 2, 4, 6					

Domain **Operations and Algebraic Thinking** *cont.*

	K	1	2	3	4	5	6
Use the relationship between addition and subtraction.		**1.OA.6** Topics 2, 4, 6					
Fluently add within 20 using mental strategies.			**2.OA.2** Topic 2				
Fluently subtract within 20 using mental strategies.			**2.OA.2** Topic 3				
Work with addition and subtraction equations.							
Understand the meaning of the equal sign.		**1.OA.7** Topics 1, 2					
Determine if equations involving addition are true or false.		**1.OA.7** Topics 4, 5					
Determine if equations involving subtraction are true or false.		**1.OA.7** Topics 2, 6					
Determine the unknown whole number in an addition equation.		**1.OA.8** Topics 1, 4–6					
Determine the unknown whole number in a subtraction equation.		**1.OA.8** Topics 2, 4, 6					
Work with equal groups of objects to gain foundations for multiplication.							
Work with even and odd numbers.			**2.OA.3** Topic 5				
Express an even number as a sum of two equal addends.			**2.OA.3** Topic 5				
Use addition to find the total number of objects in rectangular arrays.			**2.OA.4** Topic 4				
Represent and solve problems involving multiplication and division.							
Interpret products of whole numbers.				**3.OA.1** Topic 4			
Interpret whole-number quotients of whole numbers.				**3.OA.2** Topic 7			
Use multiplication within 100 to solve word problems.				**3.OA.3** Topics 4–6			
Use division within 100 to solve word problems.				**3.OA.3** Topics 7, 8			
Determine the unknown whole number in a multiplication equation.				**3.OA.4** Topics 7, 8			
Determine the unknown whole number in a division equation.				**3.OA.4** Topics 7, 8			
Understand properties of multiplication and the relationship between multiplication and division.							
Apply properties of multiplication.				**3.OA.5** Topics 4, 6			
Apply properties of division.				**3.OA.5** Topic 8			
Understand division as an unknown-factor problem.				**3.OA.6** Topic 7			
Multiply and divide within 100.							
Fluently multiply within 100.				**3.OA.7** Topic 5			
Fluently divide within 100.				**3.OA.7** Topic 8			
Solve problems involving the four operations, and identify and explain patterns in arithmetic.							
Solve two-step word problems.				**3.OA.8** Topics 2, 3, 5, 6, 8			
Assess the reasonableness of answers to two-step word problems.				**3.OA.8** Topics 2, 3, 5, 6, 8			

Domain **Operations and Algebraic Thinking** *cont.*

	K	1	2	3	4	5	6
Identify and explain arithmetic patterns.				**3.OA.9** Topics 2, 4, 5, 7			
Use the four operations with whole numbers to solve problems.							
Relate multiplication equations to multiplicative comparison.					**4.OA.1** Topic 1		
Distinguish multiplicative comparison from additive comparison.					**4.OA.2** Topics 1, 9		
Multiply to solve word problems involving multiplicative comparison.					**4.OA.2** Topics 1, 9		
Divide to solve word problems involving multiplicative comparison.					**4.OA.2** Topics 1, 9		
Solve multi-step word problems.					**4.OA.3** Topics 1, 4–10		
Assess the reasonableness of answers to multi-step word problems.					**4.OA.3** Topics 1, 4–10		
Use algebraic equations to represent multi-step word problems.					**4.OA.3** Topics 1, 4–10		
Write and interpret numerical expressions.							
Use parentheses, brackets, or braces in numerical expressions.						**5.OA.1** Topics 3, 8	
Evaluate numerical expressions with parentheses, brackets, or braces.						**5.OA.1** Topics 3, 8	
Write numerical expressions that record calculations.						**5.OA.2** Topics 3, 4, 8	
Interpret numerical expressions.						**5.OA.2** Topics 3, 4, 8	
Gain familiarity with factors and multiples.							
Find factor pairs.					**4.OA.4** Topics 1, 11		
Recognize that a whole number is a multiple of each of its factors.					**4.OA.4** Topics 1, 11		
Determine whether one number is a multiple of another.					**4.OA.4** Topics 1, 11		
Identify prime or composite numbers.					**4.OA.4** Topic 11		
Generate and analyze patterns.							
Generate a number pattern that follows a given rule.					**4.OA.5** Topics 1, 2, 11, 16		
Generate a shape pattern that follows a given rule.					**4.OA.5** Topic 2		
Describe features of a pattern.					**4.OA.5** Topic 2		
Analyze patterns and relationships.							
Generate two numerical patterns using two given rules.						**5.OA.3** Topics 8, 16	
Identify relationships between corresponding terms in two numerical patterns.						**5.OA.3** Topics 8, 16	
Form ordered pairs from two numerical patterns.						**5.OA.3** Topic 16	
Graph ordered pairs generated by two patterns.						**5.OA.3** Topic 16	

Domain **Expressions and Equations**

	K	1	2	3	4	5	6
Apply and extend previous understandings of arithmetic to algebraic expressions.							
Write numerical expressions with exponents.							**6.EE.1** Topic 1
Evaluate numerical expressions with exponents.							**6.EE.1** Topic 1
Read and write algebraic expressions.							**6.EE.2** Topic 2
Evaluate algebraic expressions.							**6.EE.2** Topic 2
Write algebraic expressions that record operations.							**6.EE.2.a** Topic 2
Identify parts of an expression using mathematical terms.							**6.EE.2.b** Topic 2
View one or more parts of an expression as a single entity.							**6.EE.2.b** Topic 2
Evaluate expressions at specific values of their variables.							**6.EE.2.c** Topics 2, 3, 17
Evaluate expressions that arise from formulas.							**6.EE.2.c** Topic 17
Evaluate expressions using Order of Operations.							**6.EE.2.c** Topics 2, 3, 17
Generate equivalent expressions.							**6.EE.3** Topics 2, 4
Identify when two expressions are equivalent.							**6.EE.4** Topic 4
Reason about and solve one-variable equations and inequalities.							
Determine the values from a specified set that make an equation true.							**6.EE.5** Topics 3, 4
Determine the values from a specified set that make an inequality true.							**6.EE.5** Topics 3, 15
Solve problems by using variables to represent numbers and write expressions.							**6.EE.6** Topics 2–4
Understand how variables are used.							**6.EE.6** Topics 2–4
Write and solve equations of the form $x + p = q$.							**6.EE.7** Topics 4, 9, 15, 17
Write and solve equations of the form $px = q$.							**6.EE.7** Topics 4, 9, 15, 17
Write an inequality of the form $x > c$ or $x < c$.							**6.EE.8** Topic 15
Recognize that inequalities of the form $x > c$ or $x < c$ have infinitely many solutions.							**6.EE.8** Topic 15
Represent solutions of inequalities on number lines.							**6.EE.8** Topic 15
Represent and analyze quantitative relationships between dependent and independent variables.							
Use variables to represent two quantities that change in relationship to one another.							**6.EE.9** Topics 11, 12, 15
Analyze relationships between dependent and independent variables.							**6.EE.9** Topics 11, 12, 15

Domain **Number and Operations in Base Ten**

	K	1	2	3	4	5	6
Work with numbers 11–19 to gain foundations for place value.							
Compose and decompose numbers from 11 to 19 into ten ones and some further ones.	**K.NBT.1** Topics 10, 11						
Record composition or decomposition.	**K.NBT.1** Topics 10, 11						
Understand that numbers from 11 to 19 are composed of ten ones and one to nine ones.	**K.NBT.1** Topics 10, 11						
Extend the counting sequence.							
Count to 120 from a given number.		**1.NBT.1** Topic 7					
Read and write numerals to 120.		**1.NBT.1** Topic 7					
Represent up to 120 objects with a written numeral.		**1.NBT.1** Topic 7					
Understand place value.							
Understand that the two digits of a two-digit number represent amounts of tens and ones.		**1.NBT.2** Topics 7–9					
Understand that 10 can be thought of as a bundle of ten ones — called a "ten."		**1.NBT.2.a** Topics 7, 8					
Understand that numbers from 11 to 19 are composed of ten ones and one to nine ones.		**1.NBT.2.b** Topic 7					
Understand that the numbers 10, 20, ... 90 refer to one to nine tens (and 0 ones).		**1.NBT.2.c** Topics 7, 8					
Compare two two-digit numbers and use the symbols >, =, and <.		**1.NBT.3** Topic 9					
Understand that the digits of a three-digit number represent amounts of hundreds, tens, and ones.			**2.NBT.1** Topic 10				
Understand that 100 can be thought of as a bundle of ten tens — called a "hundred."			**2.NBT.1.a** Topic 10				
Understand that the numbers 100, 200, ... 900 refer to one to nine hundreds (and 0 tens and 0 ones).			**2.NBT.1.b** Topic 5				
Count within 1000.			**2.NBT.2** Topics 5, 6, 10				
Skip-count by 5s, 10s, and 100s.			**2.NBT.2** Topic 10				
Read and write base-ten numerals to 1000.			**2.NBT.3** Topics 5, 10				
Read and write number names to 1000.			**2.NBT.3** Topics 5, 10				
Use expanded form for numbers to 1000.			**2.NBT.3** Topic 10				
Compare two three-digit numbers and use the symbols >, =, and <.			**2.NBT.4** Topics 5, 10				
Generalize place value understanding for multi-digit whole numbers.							
Recognize that a digit in one place represents ten times what it represents in the place to its right.					**4.NBT.1** Topics 3, 10		
Read and write base-ten numerals for multi-digit numbers.					**4.NBT.2** Topic 3		
Read and write number names for multi-digit numbers.					**4.NBT.2** Topic 3		
Use expanded form for multi-digit numbers.					**4.NBT.2** Topic 3		
Compare two multi-digit numbers and use the symbols >, =, and <.					**4.NBT.2** Topic 3		

Domain **Number and Operations in Base Ten** *cont.*

	K	1	2	3	4	5	6
Round multi-digit whole numbers to any place.					**4.NBT.3** Topics 3–7		
Understand the place value system.							
Understand how the value of a digit in one place compares to the value in the place to its right or left.						**5.NBT.1** Topics 1, 6, 7	
Explain patterns of zeros when multiplying a number by powers of 10.						**5.NBT.2** Topics 3, 6	
Use exponents to denote powers of 10.						**5.NBT.2** Topics 3, 6, 7	
Explain patterns in the placement of the decimal point when a decimal is multiplied by a power of 10.						**5.NBT.2** Topic 6	
Explain patterns in the placement of the decimal point when a decimal is divided by a power of 10.						**5.NBT.2** Topic 7	
Read and write decimals to thousandths.						**5.NBT.3** Topic 1	
Compare decimals to thousandths.						**5.NBT.3** Topic 1	
Read and write decimals to thousandths using base-ten numerals and number names.						**5.NBT.3.a** Topic 1	
Use expanded form for decimals.						**5.NBT.3.a** Topic 1	
Compare decimals to thousandths using the symbols >, =, and <.						**5.NBT.3.b** Topic 1	
Round decimals to any place.						**5.NBT.4** Topic 2	
Use place value understanding and properties of operations to add and subtract.							
Add a two-digit number and a one-digit number.		**1.NBT.4** Topics 9, 10					
Add a two-digit number and a multiple of 10.		**1.NBT.4** Topics 9, 10					
Understand place-value concepts involved in adding two-digit numbers.		**1.NBT.4** Topics 9, 10					
Mentally find 10 more than a given number.		**1.NBT.5** Topics 9, 10					
Mentally find 10 less than a given number.		**1.NBT.5** Topics 9, 11					
Subtract multiples of 10.		**1.NBT.6** Topic 11					
Fluently add within 100.			**2.NBT.5** Topics 1–3, 5–9				
Fluently subtract within 100.			**2.NBT.5** Topics 1–3, 5–9				
Add up to four two-digit numbers.			**2.NBT.6** Topics 5, 8, 9				
Understand written methods for adding within 1000.			**2.NBT.7** Topics 7, 11				
Understand place-value concepts for addition within 1000.			**2.NBT.7** Topics 7, 11				
Subtract within 1000.			**2.NBT.7** Topics 7, 11				
Understand place-value concepts for subtraction within 1000.			**2.NBT.7** Topics 7, 11				
Mentally add 10 or 100.			**2.NBT.8** Topics 6, 10, 11				

Domain **Number and Operations in Base Ten** *cont.*

	K	1	2	3	4	5	6
Mentally subtract 10 or 100.			**2.NBT.8** Topics 7, 10, 11				
Explain why addition strategies work.			**2.NBT.9** Topics 2, 5, 8, 11, 14				
Explain why subtraction strategies work.			**2.NBT.9** Topics 3, 5, 7, 9, 11, 14				
Use place value understanding and properties of operations to perform multi-digit arithmetic.							
Round whole numbers to the nearest 10.				**3.NBT.1** Topics 1–3			
Round whole numbers to the nearest 100.				**3.NBT.1** Topics 1–3			
Fluently add within 1000.				**3.NBT.2** Topics 1–3			
Fluently subtract within 1000.				**3.NBT.2** Topics 1–3			
Fluently subtract within 1000 using the relationship between addition and subtraction.				**3.NBT.2** Topics 1–3			
Multiply one-digit whole numbers by multiples of 10.				**3.NBT.3** Topic 5			
Fluently add multi-digit whole numbers using the standard algorithm.					**4.NBT.4** Topic 4		
Fluently subtract multi-digit whole numbers using the standard algorithm.					**4.NBT.4** Topic 4		
Multiply up to a four-digit number by a one-digit number.					**4.NBT.5** Topics 5–10		
Multiply two two-digit numbers.					**4.NBT.5** Topics 7–10		
Model multi-digit multiplication.					**4.NBT.5** Topics 5–10		
Divide up to four-digit dividends by one-digit divisors.					**4.NBT.6** Topics 9, 10		
Model division of up to four-digit dividends by one-digit divisors.					**4.NBT.6** Topics 9, 10		
Perform operations with multi-digit whole numbers and with decimals to hundredths.							
Fluently multiply multi-digit whole numbers using the standard algorithm.						**5.NBT.5** Topic 3	
Divide up to four-digit dividends by two-digit divisors.						**5.NBT.6** Topic 5	
Model division of up to four-digit dividends by two-digit divisors.						**5.NBT.6** Topics 4, 5	
Add decimals to hundredths.						**5.NBT.7** Topic 2	
Subtract decimals to hundredths.						**5.NBT.7** Topic 2	
Subtract decimals using the relationship between addition and subtraction.						**5.NBT.7** Topic 2	
Multiply decimals to hundredths.						**5.NBT.7** Topic 6	
Divide decimals to hundredths.						**5.NBT.7** Topic 7	
Explain strategies used to perform decimal operations.						**5.NBT.7** Topics 2, 6, 7	

Domain **Number and Operations—Fractions**

	K	1	2	3	4	5	6
Develop understanding of fractions as numbers.							
Interpret proper fractions.				**3.NF.1** Topic 9			
Relate fractions to numbers on the number line.				**3.NF.2** Topics 9, 10			
Interpret and show unit fractions on the number line.				**3.NF.2.a** Topic 9			
Interpret and show fractions of the form a/b on the number line.				**3.NF.2.b** Topic 9			
Explain equivalence of fractions.				**3.NF.3** Topic 10			
Compare fractions by reasoning about their size.				**3.NF.3** Topic 10			
Relate fraction equivalence to size.				**3.NF.3.a** Topic 10			
Relate fraction equivalence to the number line.				**3.NF.3.a** Topic 10			
Generate and model equivalent fractions.				**3.NF.3.b** Topic 10			
Relate whole numbers and fractions.				**3.NF.3.c** Topic 10			
Compare two fractions with the same numerator or same denominator and use the symbols $>$, $=$, or $<$.				**3.NF.3.d** Topic 10			
Extend understanding of fraction equivalence and ordering.							
Explain why a fraction a/b is equivalent to a fraction $(n \times a)/(n \times b)$.					**4.NF.1** Topic 11		
Recognize and generate equivalent fractions.					**4.NF.1** Topic 11		
Compare two fractions with different numerators and different denominators and use the symbols $>$, $=$, or $<$.					**4.NF.2** Topic 11		
Build fractions from unit fractions by applying and extending previous understandings of operations on whole numbers.							
Understand a fraction a/b with $a > 1$ as a sum of fractions $1/b$.					**4.NF.3** Topic 12		
Interpret addition of fractions.					**4.NF.3.a** Topic 12		
Interpret subtraction of fractions.					**4.NF.3.a** Topic 12		
Decompose fractions.					**4.NF.3.b** Topic 12		
Add mixed numbers with like denominators.					**4.NF.3.c** Topic 12		
Subtract mixed numbers with like denominators.					**4.NF.3.c** Topic 12		
Solve word problems involving addition of fractions with like denominators.					**4.NF.3.d** Topic 12		
Solve word problems involving subtraction of fractions with like denominators.					**4.NF.3.d** Topic 12		
Multiply a fraction by a whole number.					**4.NF.4** Topic 13		
Understand a fraction a/b as a multiple of $1/b$.					**4.NF.4.a** Topic 13		
Understand that $n \times (a/b) = (n \times a)/b$.					**4.NF.4.b** Topic 13		
Solve word problems involving multiplication of a fraction by a whole number.					**4.NF.4.c** Topic 13		
Understand decimal notation for fractions, and compare decimal fractions.							
Express a fraction with denominator 10 as an equivalent fraction with denominator 100.					**4.NF.5** Topic 13		

Domain **Number and Operations—Fractions** *cont.*

	K	1	2	3	4	5	6
Use equivalent fractions to add two fractions with respective denominators 10 and 100.					**4.NF.5** Topic 13		
Use decimal notation for fractions with denominators 10 or 100.					**4.NF.6** Topic 13		
Use decimal notation to describe length.					**4.NF.6** Topic 13		
Show decimals on a number line.					**4.NF.6** Topic 13		
Compare two decimals to hundredths and use the symbols >, =, and <.					**4.NF.7** Topic 13		
Use equivalent fractions as a strategy to add and subtract fractions.							
Add fractions with unlike denominators.						**5.NF.1** Topic 9	
Add mixed numbers with unlike denominators.						**5.NF.1** Topic 10	
Subtract fractions with unlike denominators.						**5.NF.1** Topic 9	
Subtract mixed numbers with unlike denominators.						**5.NF.1** Topic 10	
Solve word problems involving addition of fractions.						**5.NF.2** Topics 9, 10	
Solve word problems involving subtraction of fractions.						**5.NF.2** Topics 9, 10	
Estimate mentally and assess the reasonableness of a fraction sum or difference.						**5.NF.2** Topics 9, 10	
Apply and extend previous understandings of multiplication and division to multiply and divide fractions.							
Interpret a fraction as division.						**5.NF.3** Topic 11	
Solve word problems involving division of whole numbers with answers that are fractions or mixed numbers.						**5.NF.3** Topic 11	
Multiply a whole number by a fraction.						**5.NF.4** Topic 11	
Multiply a fraction by a fraction.						**5.NF.4** Topic 11	
Interpret the product of a fraction and a whole number.						**5.NF.4.a** Topic 11	
Relate multiplication of fractions and the area of a rectangle with fractional side lengths.						**5.NF.4.b** Topic 11	
Interpret multiplication as scaling (resizing).						**5.NF.5** Topic 11	
Predict the size of a product compared to the size of one factor on the basis of the size of the other factor.						**5.NF.5.a** Topic 11	
Explain the effect of multiplying a given number by a fraction greater than 1, less than 1, or equal to 1.						**5.NF.5.b** Topic 11	
Solve real-world problems involving multiplication of fractions.						**5.NF.6** Topic 11	
Solve real-world problems involving multiplication of mixed numbers.						**5.NF.6** Topic 11	
Divide whole numbers and unit fractions.						**5.NF.7** Topic 11	
Interpret division of a unit fraction by a whole number.						**5.NF.7.a** Topic 11	
Interpret division of a whole number by a unit fraction.						**5.NF.7.b** Topic 11	
Solve real-world problems involving division of fractions and whole numbers.						**5.NF.7.c** Topic 11	

Domain **The Number System**

	K	1	2	3	4	5	6
Apply and extend previous understandings of multiplication and division to divide fractions by fractions.							
Divide fractions.							**6.NS.1** Topic 9
Solve word problems involving division of fractions by fractions.							**6.NS.1** Topic 9
Compute fluently with multi-digit numbers and find common factors and multiples.							
Fluently divide multi-digit numbers using the standard algorithm.							**6.NS.2** Topics 3, 4
Fluently add multi-digit decimals using the standard algorithm.							**6.NS.3** Topics 3, 6
Fluently subtract multi-digit decimals using the standard algorithm.							**6.NS.3** Topics 3, 6
Fluently multiply multi-digit decimals using the standard algorithm.							**6.NS.3** Topics 3, 6
Fluently divide decimals using the standard algorithm.							**6.NS.3** Topics 3, 6
Find the greatest common factor of two numbers.							**6.NS.4** Topic 5
Find the least common multiple of two numbers.							**6.NS.4** Topic 7
Use the distributive property.							**6.NS.4** Topic 5
Apply and extend previous understandings of numbers to the system of rational numbers.							
Interpret positive and negative numbers.							**6.NS.5** Topic 10
Show rational numbers on the number line.							**6.NS.6** Topics 9, 10
Show points on the number line with negative number coordinates.							**6.NS.6** Topic 10
Graph points with negative number coordinates.							**6.NS.6** Topic 10
Interpret opposites of numbers.							**6.NS.6.a** Topic 10
Relate signs of numbers in ordered pairs to quadrants of the coordinate plane.							**6.NS.6.b** Topic 10
Relate signs of numbers in ordered pairs to reflections in the coordinate plane.							**6.NS.6.b** Topic 10
Find and position integers on a horizontal or vertical number line.							**6.NS.6.c** Topic 10
Find and position pairs of integers on a coordinate plane.							**6.NS.6.c** Topic 10
Find and position pairs of rational numbers on a coordinate plane.							**6.NS.6.c** Topic 10
Order rational numbers.							**6.NS.7** Topic 10
Understand absolute value.							**6.NS.7** Topic 10
Relate inequalities to number lines.							**6.NS.7.a** Topic 10
Write, interpret, and explain ordering of rational numbers in real-world contexts.							**6.NS.7.b** Topic 10
Interpret the absolute value of a rational number.							**6.NS.7.c** Topic 10
Relate absolute value and order.							**6.NS.7.d** Topic 10
Graph points in the coordinate plane.							**6.NS.8** Topic 10
Find distances between points with the same first coordinate or the same second coordinate.							**6.NS.8** Topic 10

Domain **Ratios and Proportional Relationships**

	K	1	2	3	4	5	6
Understand ratio concepts and use ratio reasoning to solve problems.							
Understand and apply the concept of a ratio.							**6.RP.1** Topics 7, 12
Understand the concept of a unit rate.							**6.RP.2** Topics 12, 13
Use rate language.							**6.RP.2** Topics 12, 13
Solve problems involving ratios.							**6.RP.3** Topics 12–14
Solve problems involving rates.							**6.RP.3** Topics 12–14
Make tables of equivalent ratios.							**6.RP.3.a** Topic 13
Find missing values in tables of equivalent ratios.							**6.RP.3.a** Topic 13
On the coordinate plane, plot pairs of values given in tables of equivalent ratios.							**6.RP.3.a** Topic 13
Use tables to compare ratios.							**6.RP.3.a** Topic 13
Solve unit rate problems.							**6.RP.3.b** Topics 12, 13
Find a percent of a quantity.							**6.RP.3.c** Topic 14
Find the whole, given a part and the percent.							**6.RP.3.c** Topic 14
Convert measurement units.							**6.RP.3.d** Topic 16
Transform measurement units when multiplying or dividing quantities.							**6.RP.3.d** Topic 16

Domain **Measurement and Data**

	K	1	2	3	4	5	6
Describe and compare measurable attributes.							
Describe length as a measurable attribute of objects.	**K.MD.1** Topic 12						
Describe weight as a measurable attribute of objects.	**K.MD.1** Topic 12						
Describe several measurable attributes of a single object.	**K.MD.1** Topic 12						
Directly compare and describe two objects with a measurable attribute in common.	**K.MD.2** Topic 12						
Measure lengths indirectly and by iterating length units.							
Order three objects by length.		**1.MD.1** Topic 12					
Compare the lengths of two objects indirectly by using a third object.		**1.MD.1** Topic 12					
Understand and use length units.		**1.MD.2** Topic 12					
Measure and estimate lengths in standard units.							
Use rulers, yardsticks, meter sticks, and measuring tapes.			**2.MD.1** Topic 15				
Use and analyze different length units for the same object.			**2.MD.2** Topic 15				
Estimate lengths using inches or feet.			**2.MD.3** Topic 15				
Find how much longer one object is than another in standard units.			**2.MD.4** Topic 15				
Relate addition and subtraction to length.							
Use addition to solve word problems involving lengths.			**2.MD.5** Topic 15				
Use subtraction to solve word problems involving lengths.			**2.MD.5** Topic 15				
Represent whole numbers as lengths on a number line.			**2.MD.6** Topics 8, 9				
Show sums and differences within 100 on a number line.			**2.MD.6** Topics 8, 9				
Tell and write time.							
Tell and write time in hours.		**1.MD.3** Topic 13					
Tell and write time in half-hours.		**1.MD.3** Topic 13					
Work with time and money.							
Tell and write time to the nearest five minutes.			**2.MD.7** Topic 16				
Use a.m. and p.m.			**2.MD.7** Topic 16				
Solve word problems involving dollars and cents.			**2.MD.8** Topics 13, 14				
Use $ and ¢ symbols.			**2.MD.8** Topics 13, 14				
Solve problems involving measurement and estimation of intervals of time, liquid volumes, and masses of objects.							
Tell and write time to the nearest minute.				**3.MD.1** Topic 12			
Measure time intervals in minutes.				**3.MD.1** Topic 12			
Solve word problems involving addition and subtraction of time intervals in minutes.				**3.MD.1** Topic 12			

Domain **Measurement and Data** *cont.*

	K	1	2	3	4	5	6
Represent a time problem on a number line.				**3.MD.1** Topic 12			
Measure and estimate liquid volumes using standard units of liters (l).				**3.MD.2** Topic 15			
Solve one-step word problems involving liquid volumes.				**3.MD.2** Topic 15			
Solve problems involving measurement and conversion of measurements from a larger unit to a smaller unit.							
Know relative sizes of measurement units within one system of units.					**4.MD.1** Topic 14		
Know relative sizes of units of length.					**4.MD.1** Topic 14		
Know relative sizes of units of mass.					**4.MD.1** Topic 14		
Know relative sizes of units of weight.					**4.MD.1** Topic 14		
Know relative sizes of units of liquid volume.					**4.MD.1** Topic 14		
Know relative sizes of units of time.					**4.MD.1** Topic 14		
Convert from larger units to smaller units.					**4.MD.1** Topics 13, 14		
Make a table of measurement equivalents.					**4.MD.1** Topics 13, 14		
Solve word problems involving distances.					**4.MD.2** Topics 13–15		
Solve word problems involving intervals of time.					**4.MD.2** Topics 14, 15		
Solve word problems involving liquid volumes.					**4.MD.2** Topics 14, 15		
Solve word problems involving masses of objects.					**4.MD.2** Topics 14, 15		
Solve word problems involving money.					**4.MD.2** Topics 13–15		
Use the four operations to solve measurement word problems involving simple fractions.					**4.MD.2** Topics 13–15		
Represent measurement quantities on number line diagrams.					**4.MD.2** Topics 13–15		
Use the area formula for rectangles.					**4.MD.3** Topic 15		
Use the perimeter formula for rectangles.					**4.MD.3** Topic 15		
Convert like measurement units within a given measurement system.							
Convert measurement units.						**5.MD.1** Topic 13	
Use conversions to solve real-world problems.						**5.MD.1** Topic 13	
Geometric measurement: understand concepts of area and relate area to multiplication and to addition.							
Recognize area as an attribute of plane figures.				**3.MD.5** Topic 14			
Understand concepts of area measurement.				**3.MD.5** Topic 14			
Understand the concept of square unit.				**3.MD.5.a** Topic 14			
Relate *n* unit squares to an area of *n* square units.				**3.MD.5.b** Topic 14			
Measure areas by counting in square inches and feet.				**3.MD.6** Topic 14			

Domain **Measurement and Data** *cont.*

	K	1	2	3	4	5	6
Measure areas by counting unit squares in improvised units.				**3.MD.6** Topic 14			
Relate area to the operation of multiplication.				**3.MD.7** Topic 14			
Relate area to the operation of addition.				**3.MD.7** Topic 14			
Find the area of a rectangle by tiling it.				**3.MD.7.a** Topic 14			
Show that the area of a rectangle can be found by multiplying the side lengths.				**3.MD.7.a** Topic 14			
Multiply side lengths to find areas of rectangles.				**3.MD.7.b** Topic 14			
Represent whole-number products as rectangular areas in mathematical reasoning.				**3.MD.7.b** Topic 14			
Use tiling to show that the area of a rectangle with side lengths a and $b + c$ is the sum of $a \times b$ and $a \times c$.				**3.MD.7.c** Topics 6, 14			
Use area models to represent the distributive property.				**3.MD.7.c** Topic 14			
Find areas of rectilinear figures by decomposing them into non-overlapping rectangles.				**3.MD.7.d** Topics 6, 14			
Geometric measurement: recognize perimeter as an attribute of plane figures and distinguish between linear and area measures.							
Solve perimeter problems.				**3.MD.8** Topics 6, 13, 14			
Solve perimeter problems involving finding an unknown side length.				**3.MD.8** Topic 13			
Exhibit rectangles with the same perimeter and different areas.				**3.MD.8** Topic 13			
Exhibit rectangles with the same area and different perimeters.				**3.MD.8** Topic 14			
Geometric measurement: understand concepts of angle and measure angles.							
Understand how angles are formed.					**4.MD.5** Topic 16		
Understand concepts of angle measurement.					**4.MD.5** Topic 16		
Relate angle measurement in degrees to circles.					**4.MD.5.a** Topic 16		
Relate one-degree angles to *n*-degree angles.					**4.MD.5.b** Topic 16		
Measure angles using a protractor.					**4.MD.6** Topic 16		
Sketch angles of specified measure.					**4.MD.6** Topic 16		
Recognize angle measure as additive.					**4.MD.7** Topic 16		
Solve addition and subtraction problems to find unknown angles on a diagram.					**4.MD.7** Topic 16		
Geometric measurement: understand concepts of volume and relate volume to multiplication and to addition.							
Recognize volume as an attribute of solid figures.						**5.MD.3** Topic 12	
Understand concepts of volume measurement.						**5.MD.3** Topic 12	
Understand the concept of cubic unit.						**5.MD.3.a** Topic 12	
Relate *n* unit cubes to a volume of *n* cubic units.						**5.MD.3.b** Topic 12	

Domain **Measurement and Data** *cont.*

	K	1	2	3	4	5	6
Measure volumes by counting in cubic inches and feet.						**5.MD.4** Topic 12	
Measure volumes by counting unit cubes in improvised units.						**5.MD.4** Topic 12	
Relate volume to the operations of multiplication and addition.						**5.MD.5** Topic 12	
Solve real-world and mathematical problems involving volume.						**5.MD.5** Topic 12	
Show that the volume of a right rectangular prism can be found by multiplying the edge lengths.						**5.MD.5.a** Topic 12	
Show that the volume of a right rectangular prism can be found by multiplying the height by the area of the base.						**5.MD.5.a** Topic 12	
Represent threefold whole-number products as volumes.						**5.MD.5.a** Topic 12	
Use the formulas $V = \ell \times w \times h$ and $V = b \times h$ for rectangular prisms.						**5.MD.5.b** Topic 12	
Find volumes of solid figures composed of two non-overlapping right rectangular prisms.						**5.MD.5.c** Topic 12	
Classify objects and count the number of objects in each category.							
Classify objects into given categories.	**K.MD.3** Topics 9, 13						
Count the numbers of objects in a category.	**K.MD.3** Topics 9, 13						
Sort categories by count.	**K.MD.3** Topics 9, 13						
Represent and interpret data.							
Organize, represent, interpret, and compare data with up to three categories.		**1.MD.4** Topic 14					
Measure objects to generate whole-number length data.			**2.MD.9** Topic 16				
Make repeated measurements of the same object to generate length data.			**2.MD.9** Topic 16				
Draw a picture graph to represent a data set with up to four categories.			**2.MD.10** Topic 16				
Draw a bar graph with up to four categories.			**2.MD.10** Topic 16				
Solve problems using data presented in a bar graph.			**2.MD.10** Topic 16				
Draw a scaled picture graph to represent a data set with several categories.				**3.MD.3** Topic 16			
Draw a scaled bar graph to represent a data set with several categories.				**3.MD.3** Topic 16			
Solve problems using information presented in scaled bar graphs.				**3.MD.3** Topic 16			
Find lengths involving halves and fourths of a unit and display them in a line plot.				**3.MD.4** Topic 16			
Solve problems involving addition and subtraction of fractions by using measurement data in line plots.					**4.MD.4** Topic 15		
Make a line plot to display measurements involving halves, fourths, and eighths of a unit.					**4.MD.4** Topic 15		
Solve problems involving fraction operations by using measurement data in line plots.						**5.MD.2** Topic 14	

Domain **Statistics and Probability**

	K	1	2	3	4	5	6
Develop understanding of statistical variability.							
Understand statistical questions.							**6.SP.1** Topic 19
Understand how data are described by a measure of center.							**6.SP.2** Topic 19
Understand how data are described by their spread.							**6.SP.2** Topic 19
Understand how data are described by the overall shape.							**6.SP.2** Topic 19
Understand how a measure of center describes the data values.							**6.SP.3** Topic 19
Understand how a measure of variability describes how the data values in a set vary.							**6.SP.3** Topic 19
Summarize and describe distributions.							
Display numerical data in plots on a number line.							**6.SP.4** Topic 19
Display numerical data in dot plots.							**6.SP.4** Topic 19
Display numerical data in histograms.							**6.SP.4** Topic 19
Display numerical data in box plots.							**6.SP.4** Topic 19
Summarize numerical data in relation to their context.							**6.SP.5** Topic 19
For numerical data, report the number of observations.							**6.SP.5.a** Topic 19
For numerical data, describe the nature of the attribute under investigation.							**6.SP.5.b** Topic 19
For numerical data, describe how the investigated attribute was measured and its units of measurement.							**6.SP.5.b** Topic 19
Find the median of a set of data.							**6.SP.5.c** Topic 19
Find the mean of a set of data.							**6.SP.5.c** Topic 19
Find the interquartile range and/or mean absolute deviation of a data set.							**6.SP.5.c** Topic 19
Describe overall patterns or deviations in a data set.							**6.SP.5.c** Topic 19
Relate a measure of center to the shape of the data distribution and context of data collection.							**6.SP.5.d** Topic 19
Relate a measure of variability to the shape of the data distribution and context of data collection.							**6.SP.5.d** Topic 19

Domain Geometry

	K	1	2	3	4	5	6
Identify and describe shapes (squares, circles, triangles, rectangles, hexagons, cubes, cones, cylinders, and spheres).							
Describe shapes in the environment.	**K.G.1** Topic 15						
Describe position.	**K.G.1** Topic 15						
Correctly name shapes regardless of their orientations.	**K.G.2** Topics 14, 16						
Correctly name shapes regardless of their overall size.	**K.G.2** Topics 14, 16						
Identify two-dimensional shapes as flat.	**K.G.3** Topics 14, 16						
Identify three-dimensional shapes as solid.	**K.G.3** Topics 14, 16						
Analyze, compare, create, and compose shapes.							
Analyze and compare two- and three-dimensional shapes in different sizes.	**K.G.4** Topic 16						
Analyze and compare two- and three-dimensional shapes in different orientations.	**K.G.4** Topic 16						
Build and draw shapes to model shapes in the world.	**K.G.5** Topic 16						
Compose simple shapes to form larger shapes.	**K.G.6** Topic 16						
Reason with shapes and their attributes.							
Distinguish between defining attributes versus non-defining attributes.		**1.G.1** Topic 15					
Build and draw shapes with defining attributes.		**1.G.1** Topic 15					
Compose two- and three-dimensional shapes.		**1.G.2** Topic 15					
Compose new shapes from composite shapes.		**1.G.2** Topic 15					
Partition circles and rectangles into two equal shares and use related vocabulary.		**1.G.3** Topic 16					
Partition circles and rectangles into four equal shares and use related vocabulary.		**1.G.3** Topic 16					
Recognize that decomposing shapes into more equal shares creates smaller shares.		**1.G.3** Topic 16					
Recognize and draw two- and three-dimensional shapes having specified attributes.			**2.G.1** Topic 12				
Identify triangles, quadrilaterals, pentagons, hexagons, and cubes.			**2.G.1** Topic 12				
Partition a rectangle into rows and columns of same-size squares and count the squares.			**2.G.2** Topic 12				
Partition circles and rectangles into two, three, or four equal shares, and use related vocabulary.			**2.G.3** Topic 12				
Recognize that equal shares of identical wholes need not have the same shape.			**2.G.3** Topic 12				
Understand that shapes in different categories may share attributes.				**3.G.1** Topic 11			
Understand that shared attributes of shapes can define a larger category.				**3.G.1** Topic 11			
Recognize rhombuses, rectangles, and squares as examples of quadrilaterals and draw quadrilaterals that are non-examples.				**3.G.1** Topic 11			
Partition shapes into parts with equal areas.				**3.G.2** Topics 11, 14			
Express the area of each equal part of a shape as a unit fraction of the whole.				**3.G.2** Topics 11, 14			

Domain **Geometry** *cont.*

	K	1	2	3	4	5	6
Draw and identify lines and angles, and classify shapes by properties of their lines and angles.							
Draw and identify points, lines, line segments, and rays.					**4.G.1** Topic 16		
Draw and identify parallel and perpendicular lines.					**4.G.1** Topic 16		
Draw and identify angles.					**4.G.1** Topic 16		
Draw and identify right, acute, and obtuse angles.					**4.G.1** Topic 16		
Use parallel or perpendicular lines to classify figures.					**4.G.2** Topic 16		
Use angle measure to classify figures.					**4.G.2** Topic 16		
Categorize and identify right triangles.					**4.G.2** Topic 16		
Understand line symmetry.					**4.G.3** Topic 16		
Identify line-symmetric figures.					**4.G.3** Topic 16		
Draw lines of symmetry.					**4.G.3** Topic 16		
Classify two-dimensional figures into categories based on their properties.							
Understand that attributes belonging to a category of two-dimensional figures also belong to all subcategories of that category.						**5.G.3** Topic 15	
Classify two-dimensional figures in a hierarchy based on properties.						**5.G.4** Topic 15	
Graph points on the coordinate plane to solve real-world and mathematical problems.							
Understand a coordinate system.						**5.G.1** Topic 16	
Graph points in the first quadrant of the coordinate plane.						**5.G.2** Topic 16	
Interpret coordinate values of points in the first quadrant of the coordinate plane.						**5.G.2** Topic 16	
Solve real-world and mathematical problems involving area, surface area, and volume.							
Find area by composing a figure into rectangles.							**6.G.1** Topics 8, 11, 17
Find area by decomposing a figure into triangles and other shapes.							**6.G.1** Topics 8, 11, 17
Find the volume of a right rectangular prism with fractional edge lengths by packing it with unit cubes of the appropriate unit fraction edge lengths.							**6.G.2** Topic 18
Show that the volume of a right rectangular prism with fractional edge lengths can be found by multiplying the edge lengths of the prism.							**6.G.2** Topic 18
Apply the formulas $V = \ell w h$ and $V = b h$ to find volumes of right rectangular prisms with fractional edge lengths.							**6.G.2** Topic 18
Draw polygons in the coordinate plane.							**6.G.3** Topics 10, 11
Find the length of a side of a polygon drawn in the coordinate plane.							**6.G.3** Topic 11
Represent three-dimensional figures using nets.							**6.G.4** Topics 17, 18
Use nets to find the surface area of three-dimensional figures.							**6.G.4** Topic 18

Program Guide

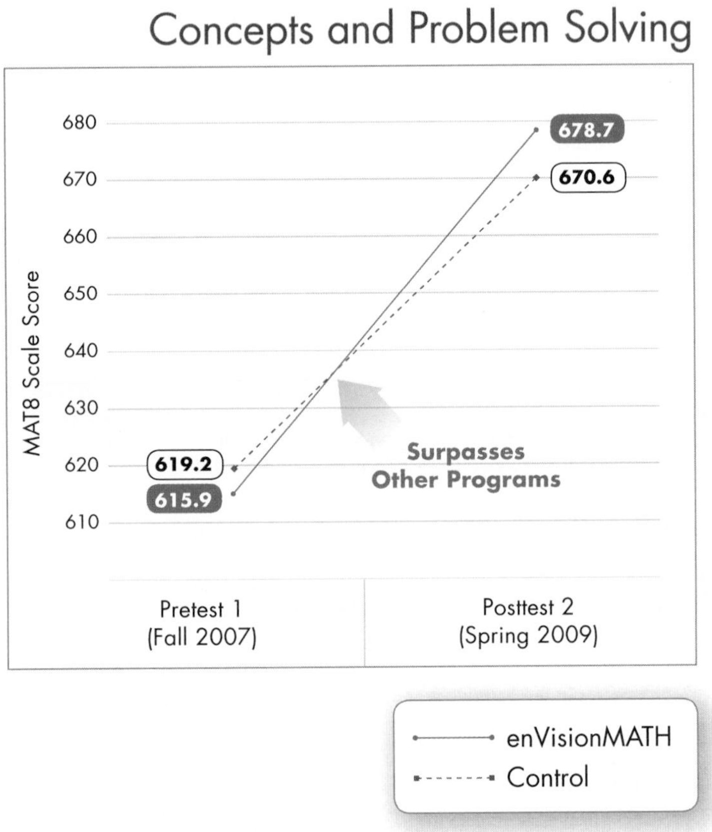

Better Conceptual Understanding and Problem Solving

enVisionMATH students were UNSURPASSED in conceptual understanding and problem solving, despite starting out at a lower level.

The difference shown in this graph is statistically significant.

Statistically More Effective

Pearson authorship team conducts a thorough review of scientific research to determine new educational practices.

Written specifically to address the Common Core State Standards, ***enVisionMATH Common Core*** is based on critical foundational research and proven classroom results.

Computation

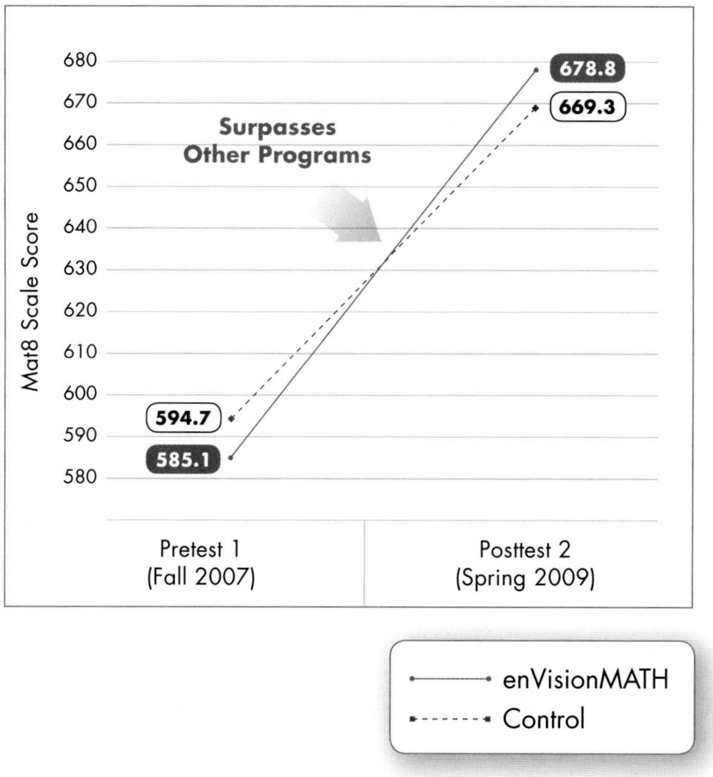

Ability Level

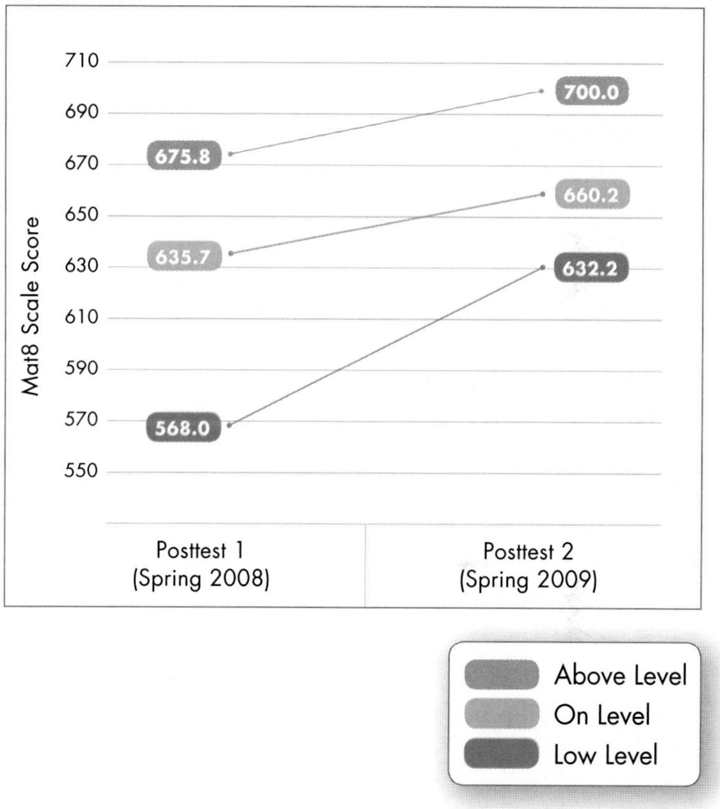

Better Computation Scores

enVisionMATH students were UNSURPASSED in computational skills, despite starting out at a lower math level.

The difference shown in this graph is statistically significant.

Better Results for All Ability Levels

All ability levels increased in mathematical achievement using *enVisionMATH*.

Low-level students showed the most gain, indicating a narrowing of the "achievement gap."

The difference shown in this graph is statistically significant.

The big ideas in ***enVisionMATH Common Core*** align closely to the Conceptual Categories and Domains of the Standards for Mathematical Content in the Common Core State Standards.

A Conversation with Grant Wiggins

Q What is Understanding by Design?

A **Understanding by Design** is a comprehensive approach to unit planning, and a series of resources on curricular planning developed by Grant Wiggins and Jay McTighe and published by the Association for Supervision and Curriculum Development (ASCD).

Q Why is it called **Understanding by Design?**

A Consider each phrase: as educators, we aim for student *understanding,* not merely the acquisition of superficial skill or knowledge. We also aim for understanding by design as opposed to having it happen by chance or by luck. What is "understanding"? It is the ability to make meaning and to transfer prior learning to new tasks. Well, if you want those two things—and what teacher doesn't?—you have to plan and design for it and not just hope it happens as an outgrowth of learning content.

Q What do you mean by saying that understanding is two things: *meaning making* and *transfer*?

A Well, those are two different, yet related parts of the word. If a student can "connect the dots" or "see patterns" or "make inferences" that go beyond the particulars, then we all agree that the student really "understands." But we also say that if a student can't apply or transfer prior learning to new and perhaps unfamiliar situations and tasks, then the student really doesn't "understand."

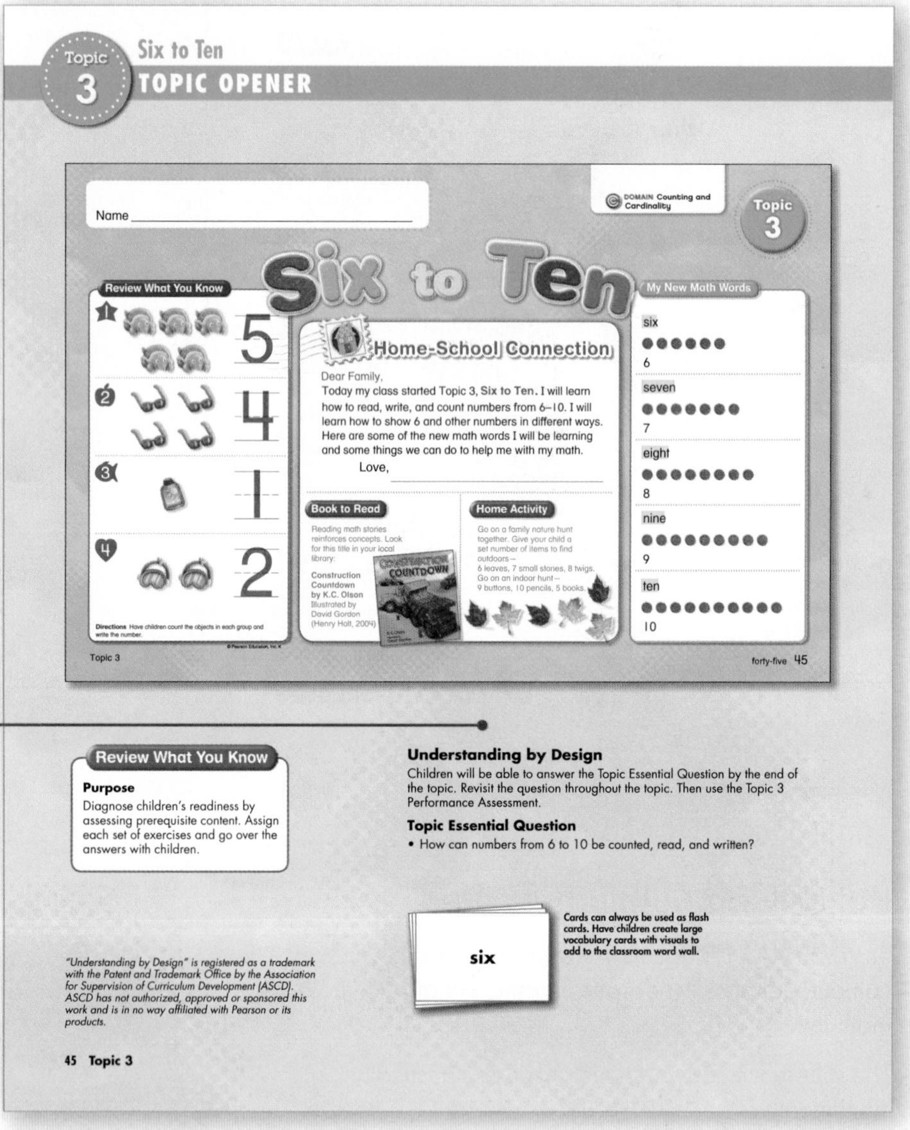
Topic 3 Six to Ten
TOPIC OPENER

Name ______

DOMAIN Counting and Cardinality

Topic 3

Six to Ten

Review What You Know

Home-School Connection

Dear Family,
Today my class started Topic 3, Six to Ten. I will learn how to read, write, and count numbers from 6–10. I will learn how to show 6 and other numbers in different ways. Here are some of the new math words I will be learning and some things we can do to help me with my math.
Love, ______

Book to Read
Reading math stories reinforces concepts. Look for this title in your local library:
Construction Countdown by K.C. Olson Illustrated by David Gordon (Henry Holt, 2004)

Home Activity
Go on a family nature hunt together. Give your child a set number of items to find outdoors—
6 leaves, 7 small stones, 8 twigs.
Go on an indoor hunt—
9 buttons, 10 pencils, 5 books.

My New Math Words
six 6
seven 7
eight 8
nine 9
ten 10

Directions Have children count the objects in each group and write the number.

Topic 3 forty-five 45

Review What You Know

Purpose
Diagnose children's readiness by assessing prerequisite content. Assign each set of exercises and go over the answers with children.

Understanding by Design
Children will be able to answer the Topic Essential Question by the end of the topic. Revisit the question throughout the topic. Then use the Topic 3 Performance Assessment.

Topic Essential Question
- How can numbers from 6 to 10 be counted, read, and written?

six

Cards can always be used as flash cards. Have children create large vocabulary cards with visuals to add to the classroom word wall.

"Understanding by Design" is registered as a trademark with the Patent and Trademark Office by the Association for Supervision of Curriculum Development (ASCD). ASCD has not authorized, approved or sponsored this work and is in no way affiliated with Pearson or its products.

45 Topic 3

▲ **Teacher's Edition**

Q Where in *enVisionMATH Common Core* are Understanding by Design principles implemented?

A *enVisionMATH Common Core* includes Understanding by Design in every

- Topic Math Background
- Topic Opener
- Lesson Overview
- Lesson Close

Q Why is Understanding by Design needed?

A To make sure that all students develop understanding, you have to deliberately and purposefully target students' abilities to ask questions, make connections, and transfer their prior learning to new tasks. Doing so requires a more explicit plan where you design "backward" from understanding—meaning making and transference—instead of "backward" from content mastery.

Q How important is "understanding" in beginning math instruction? Isn't the point just to make sure students learn the key skills?

A This is a vital issue that educators may not think through sufficiently. Skill, by itself, does not answer the question, *How and when should I use each skill?* Answering that question requires understanding. Skill and knowledge by themselves do not help students solve new and unfamiliar-looking problems.

Problem solving requires applying learning to new and unfamiliar tasks. It is like literacy instruction: students need to know what to do when they get stuck or puzzled if they are going to be successful users of mathematics skills.

Q So math is not just skills and facts?

A No, there are some big ideas that can help students make sense of everything they do and make it more likely that they can solve new problems. Here is a big idea about problem solving: P*roblem solving is turning unknowns into knowns and unfamiliars into familiars, by means of helpful equivalences.* That's the point of learning to factor, regroup, or any simplifying techniques. These techniques also help students realize, slowly but surely, what the equal sign really means.

> *"... there are some big ideas that can help students make sense of everything they do and make it more likely that they can solve new problems."*

Once students understand this idea – that is, they make it a key strategy—then they will "see" the skill work differently, with greater perspective. They will better understand the value of each new skill and be more likely to transfer their learning to new problems.

Q So, is this where big questions can be found in math—questions about problem solving?

A That's one key area for big questions: For example, W*hat kind of problem is this? What does it remind me of? What is the problem really asking, even if it doesn't say so directly?*—these are all big questions. They start out being the teacher's questions; but they have to end up, over time, being the students' questions if understanding is to occur.

Through visual learning, students make sense of problems, develop solutions to plans, and use tools appropriately, all leading to conceptual understanding.

MathStart®

Research says literature is an engaging way to help children access math concepts (Hong, 1996).

enVisionMATH Common Core references **MathStart® readers by Stuart J. Murphy** which:

- Are **fiction books** that teach math concepts through stories and visual learning strategies (sold separately from *enVisionMATH*).
- Contain **engaging stories and illustrations** that hold students' interest and show how math is relevant to their lives.
- Contain **accessible text** that is age appropriate.
- Use **visual models** that enhance conceptual understanding.
- Are useful in developing intervention strategies and in providing differentiated instruction opportunities.
- Are packaged with **Guided Problem-Solving Masters** and teacher notes.

The books in the Math Library are also available in Spanish.

A Conversation with Stuart J. Murphy

Stuart J. Murphy's background as an expert in visual learning, which inspired his work on the MathStart® series, has also played an integral role in the development of the *enVisionMATH Common Core* program.

Q What is visual learning?

A Visual learning is the acquisition, assimilation, and application of information through visual stimuli, such as charts, graphs, diagrams, illustrations, and photographs.

Q Why is visual learning important in math?

A Visual learning supports the development of critical-thinking skills and problem-solving capabilities so that students perform better in math. It builds bridges from concrete to abstract representations. Purposeful pictures include images that show the information needed to solve real-world problems. Digestible chunks give students a chance to focus on an individual math concept or a single step in a math procedure. And, the arrangement of visuals and text on a page shows how multiple concepts or ideas work together, so that students see math as cohesive and not just a set of unrelated steps.

Q How does visual learning support the Common Core State Standards?

A Visual learning is especially helpful in addressing the goals of the Mathematical Practices. Pictures and models allow students to discern patterns, see and make use of structure, understand geometric relationships, and simplify complex situations. Sketching helps students to make sense of problems, and to develop their reasoning skills. Visual images encourage students to make connections, communicate about math, and see how math relates to everyday life.

Books in the Grade K–2 Math Libraries

Grade K

- Animals on Board
- Every Buddy Counts
- Jack the Builder
- Just Enough Carrots
- Same Old Horse

Grade 1

- A Fair Bear Share
- Leaping Lizards
- 100 Days of Cool
- Spunky Monkeys on Parade
- Super Sand Castle Saturday

Grade 2

- Coyotes All Around
- Elevator Magic
- Missing Mittens
- Game Time!
- Shark Swimathon

For a complete list of books in the MathStart series appropriate for students of various ages, see the MathStart® Bibliography on p.89.

The Standards for Mathematical Practice stress the importance of strong problem-solving and reasoning abilities to develop conceptual understanding.

Problem Solving

Research says that for all content areas, conceptual understanding, computational fluency, and problem-solving skills are each essential and mutually reinforcing, influencing performance on such varied tasks as estimation, word problems, and computation (National Mathematics Advisory Panel, 2008).

enVisionMATH Common Core provides:

- **Problem-solving skills and strategies** taught in problem-solving lessons.
- **Phases in a problem-solving process** taught in problem-solving lessons. The phases are: Read and Understand, Plan and Solve, and Look Back and Check.
- **Problem-Based Interactive Learning** that supports teaching through problem solving.
- **Problems in examples** to reinforce meanings of operations.
- **A variety of problem-solving exercises** including: Think About the Structure, Reasonableness, Writing to Explain, Use Tools, and Write a Problem.
- **Problem-Solving Handbook** in front of the student book that students can go back to during the year.
- **Problem-Solving Recording Sheet** that helps students record their thinking.
- **Mixed Problem Solving** pages for more reinforcement of choosing strategies.

"A new approach to solving word problems is to use bar diagrams as visual representations that show how quantities in a word problem are related."

—Dr. Randall Charles

▲ **Student Edition**

Solve

Look Back and Check

3

_____ + _____ = _____

4

_____ + _____ = _____

ections Have children listen to the problems and then draw pictures to solve. **3.** Maria hit 5 baseballs in one inning 1 2 in the next. How many did she hit in both innings put together? **4.** Zak kicked 2 soccer balls into the goal, and then iore into the goal. How many did he kick in all?

one hundred forty 140

Bar Diagrams

Research says that bar diagrams help students understand the relationships between quantities in a problem, and this helps students choose a correct operation to solve the problem (Diezmann and English, 2001).

enVisionMATH Common Core provides:

- **Visual models for ways to make a number in Grade K** to build a foundation for addition and subtraction.

8 is 3 and 5.

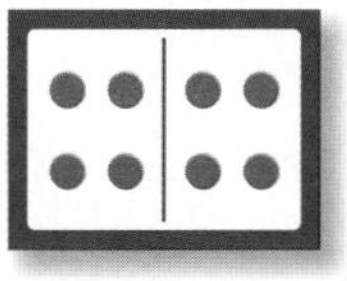
8 is 4 and 4.

- **Visual models for addition and subtraction situations in Grades 1–2** to help children see relationships between quantities. In the model, children place objects, then later draw dots, and then later write numbers.

Joining

There are 3 birds. 2 more fly in. How many in all?	There are 3 birds. More fly in. Then there are 5 in all. How many flew in?	There are some birds. 2 more fly in. Then there are 5 in all. How many were there to begin with?

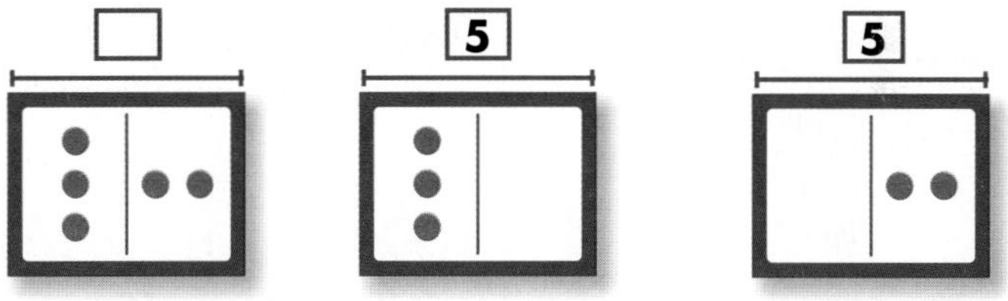

Separating

There are 7 birds. 3 birds fly away. How many are left?	There are 7 birds. Some fly away. Then 4 birds are left. How many flew away?	There are some birds. 3 birds fly away. Then 4 birds are left. How many were there to begin with?

The models help children think about joining and separating as **Part-Part-Whole**. Children add when the whole is unknown and subtract when a part is unknown. Comparison problems and joining-equal groups problems are also introduced.

Bar Diagrams: Addition-Subtraction

Joining

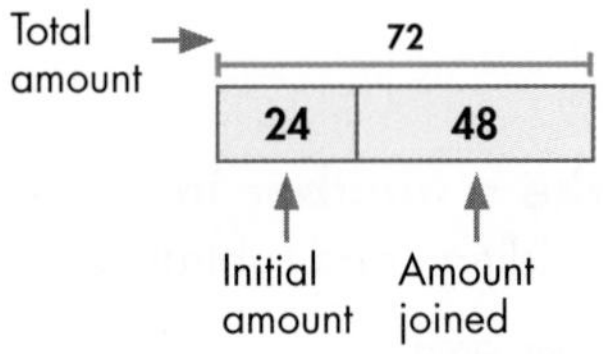

Total Amount Unknown

Kim has 23 dolls. Her father gives her 18 more dolls. Now how many dolls does she have?

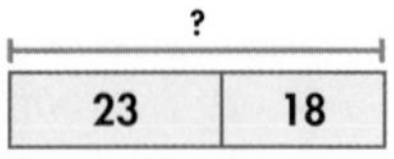

Amount Joined Unknown

Debbie has saved $57. How much more money does she need in order to have $112?

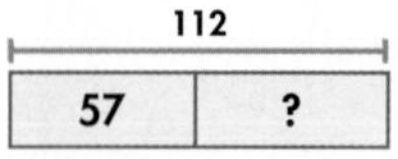

Initial Amount Unknown

Tom had some money in his savings account. He then deposited $45 into the same account. Then he had $92 in all. How much did he have in his savings account to start?

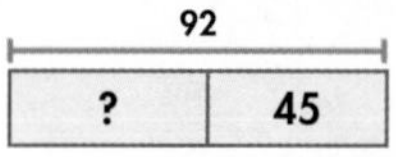

Separating

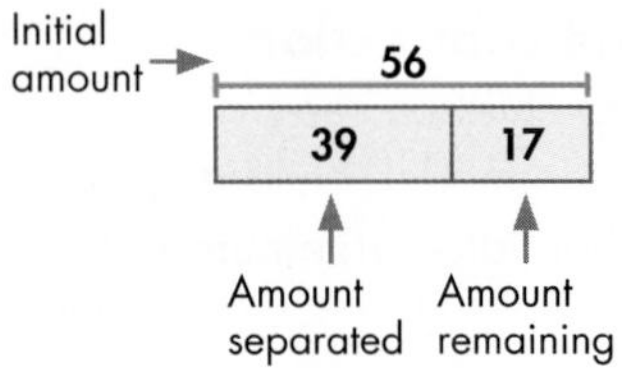

Amount Remaining Unknown

Steven had 122 peanuts. He ate 71 of them. How many peanuts are left?

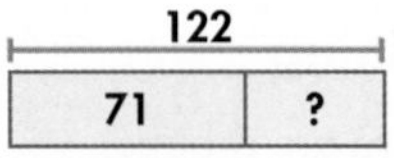

Amount Separated Unknown

Carrie had 45 CDs. She gave some to Jo. Then Carrie had 27 left. How many did she give to Jo?

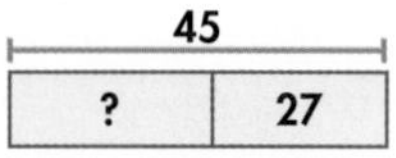

Initial Amount Unknown

Alan had some marbles. He lost 12 of them. Then he had 32 left. How many did he have to begin with?

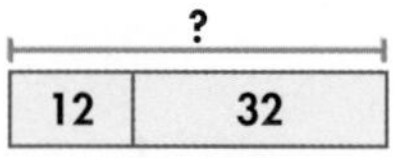

Part-Part-Whole

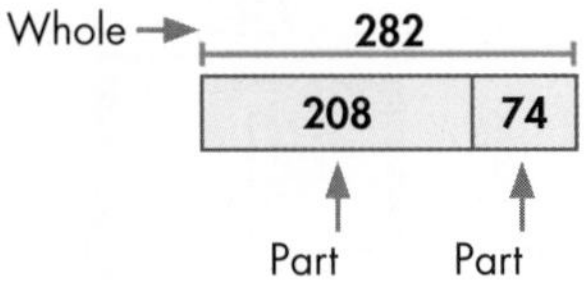

Whole Unknown

A kennel has 14 cats and 16 dogs. How many dogs and cats are in the kennel?

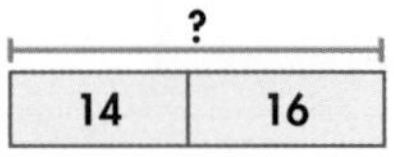

One Part Unknown

Jim has 18 wheat crackers and some rye crackers. He has 63 crackers in all. How many rye crackers does he have?

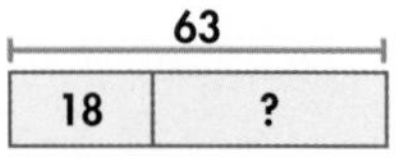

Another Part Unknown

Some adults and 12 children are on a bus. There are 31 people on the bus. How many adults are on the bus?

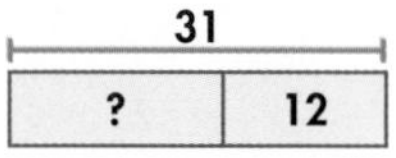

Joining and separating can be thought of as part-part-whole. You can add when the whole is unknown. You can subtract when a part is unknown.

Comparison

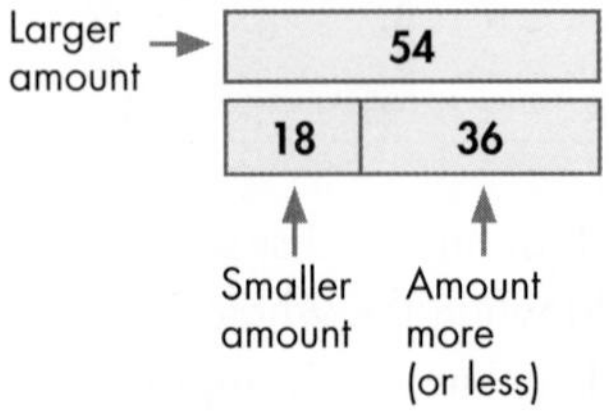

Amount More (or Less) Unknown

Alex has 47 toy cars. Keisha has 12 toy cars. How many more cars does Alex have?

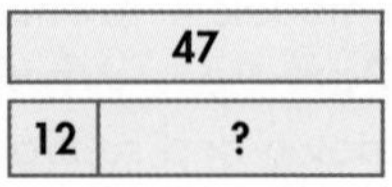

Smaller Amount Unknown

Fran spent $84 which was $26 more than Alice spent.How much did Alice spend?

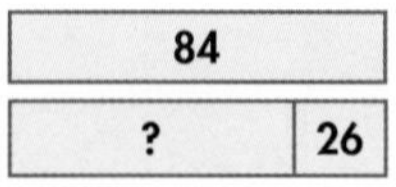

Larger Amount Unknown

Barney has 23 old coins. Steve has 16 more old coins than Barney. How many old coins does Steve have?

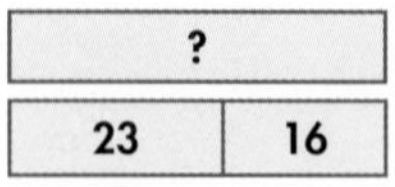

You can add when the larger amount is unknown. You can subtract when the smaller amount or the amount more (or the amount less) is unknown.

Bar Diagrams: Multiplication-Division

Joining Equal Groups

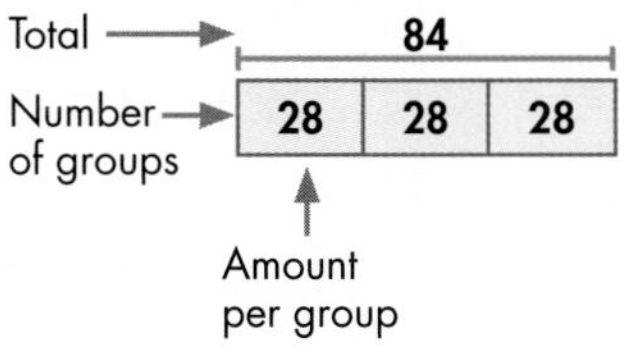

Total Amount Unknown

Kim has 4 photo albums. Each album has 85 pictures. How many photos are in her 4 albums?

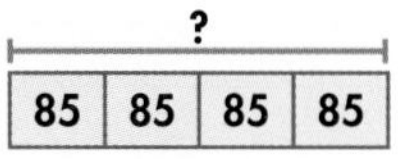

Amount Per Group Unknown

Pam put the same number of apples in each of 4 bags. She ended up with 52 apples in bags. How many apples did she put in each bag?

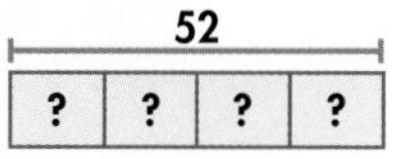

Number of Groups Unknown

Fred bought some books. Each book cost $16. He spent $80 on books. How many books did he buy?

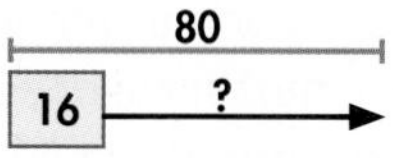

Separating Equal Groups

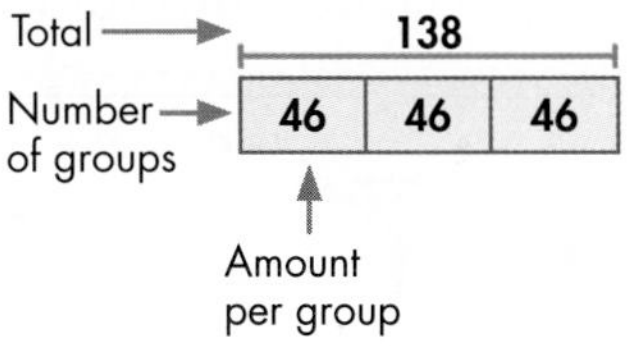

Amount Per Group Unknown

Bryan got 45 pigeons. He put them in 5 pens with the same number of pigeons in each pen. How many pigeons are in each pen?

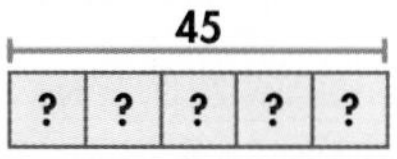

Number of Groups Unknown

A total of 108 children signed up for soccer. The coach put them into 18-person teams. How many teams were made?

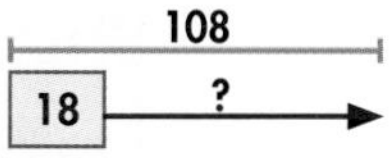

Total Amount Unknown

Kim had some cards. She put them into piles of 35 and was able to make 4 piles. How many cards did she start with?

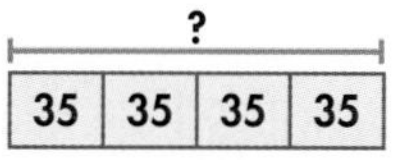

Joining or separating equal groups is like part-part-whole. You can multiply when a whole (total) is unknown. You can divide when the number of equal parts (groups) or the size of each part group is unknown.

Comparison

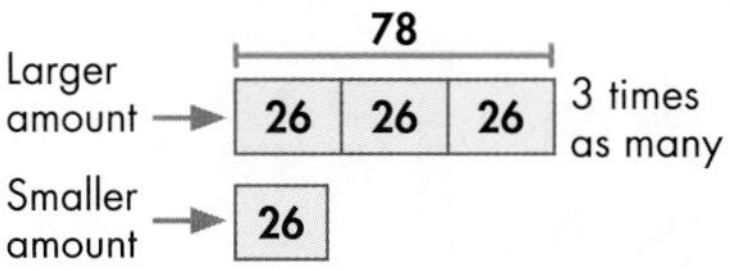

Larger Amount Unknown

Alex has 17 toy cars, Keisha has 3 times as many. How many cars does Keisha have?

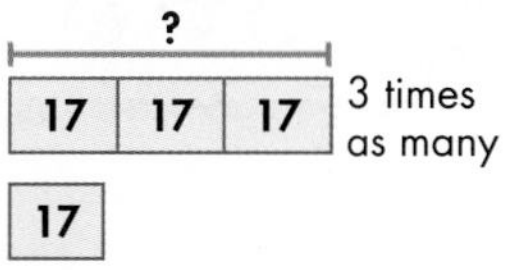

Smaller Amount Unknown

Barney has 24 old coins. This is 3 times as many coins as Steve has. How many old coins does Steve have?

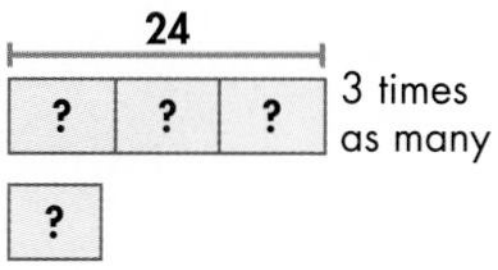

Number of Times as Many Unknown

Ann's teacher is 39 years old. Ann is 13 years old. Ann's teacher is how many times as old as Ann?

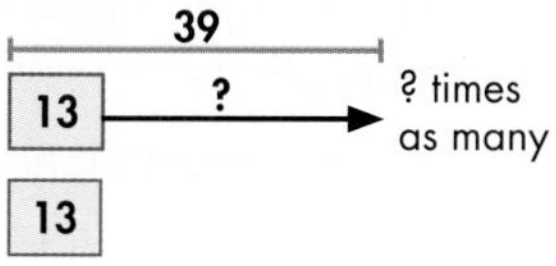

You can multiply when the larger amount is unknown. You can divide when the smaller amount or the number of times as many is unknown.

- **Focused instruction on bar diagrams** is in problem-solving lessons, in lessons on meanings of operations, and in lessons on mental math.
- **A variety of problems** as shown here are infused in lessons to help students develop the quantitative reasoning needed for success on high-stakes tests and in real life.

Algebra in Kindergarten Through Grade 6

Research says that rule-based instructional approaches that do not give students opportunities to create meaning for the rules or to learn when to use them can lead to forgetting, unsystematic errors, reliance on visual clues, and poor strategic decisions. (Mathematics Learning Study Committee, 2001)

"To prepare students for Algebra, the curriculum must simultaneously develop conceptual understanding, computational fluency, and problem-solving skills. These three aspects of learning are mutually reinforcing and should not be seen as competing for class time" (National Mathematics Advisory Panel, 2008, p. 19).

The National Mathematics Advisory Panel proposed three clusters of concepts and skills that serve as the Critical Foundation of Algebra:

(1) fluency with whole numbers,

(2) fluency with fractions, and

(3) particular aspects of geometry and measurement.

Students in Kindergarten through Grade 6 can develop the algebraic thinking skills by using **patterns** to make **generalizations,** and by using **mathematical symbols** to describe **relationships.**

enVisionMATH Common Core provides:

- lessons involving patterns and generalizations.
- multiple representations of relationships.

Kindergarten Visual Learning Bridge

Grade 1 Visual Learning Bridge

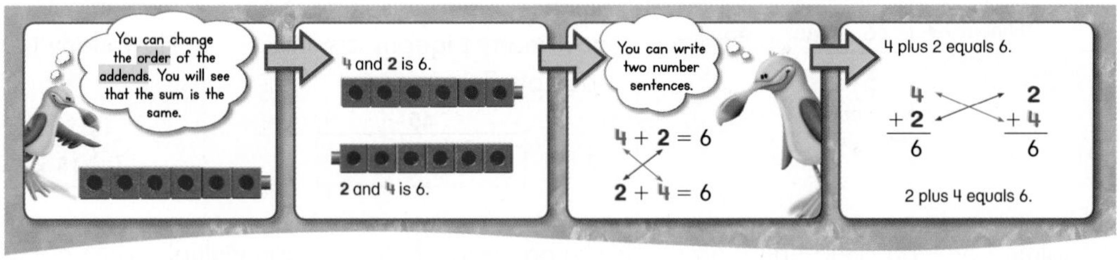

Grade 2 Visual Learning Bridge

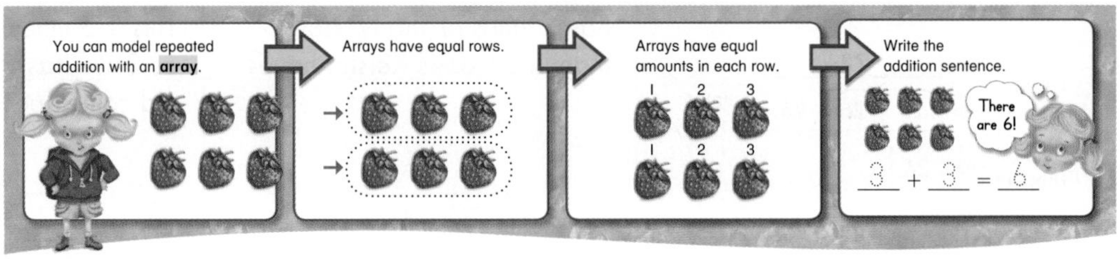

Grade 3 Visual Learning Bridge

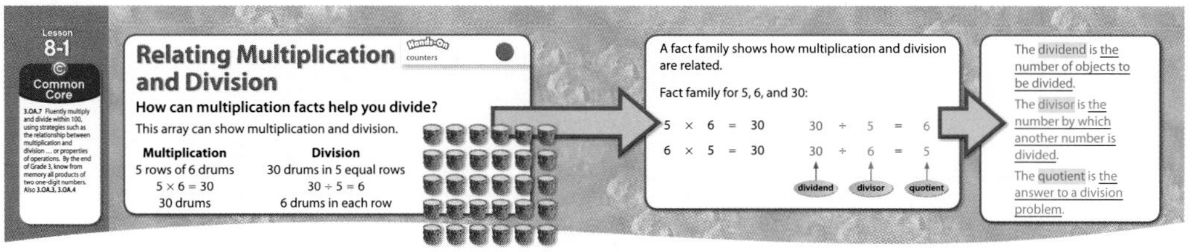

Grade 4 Visual Learning Bridge

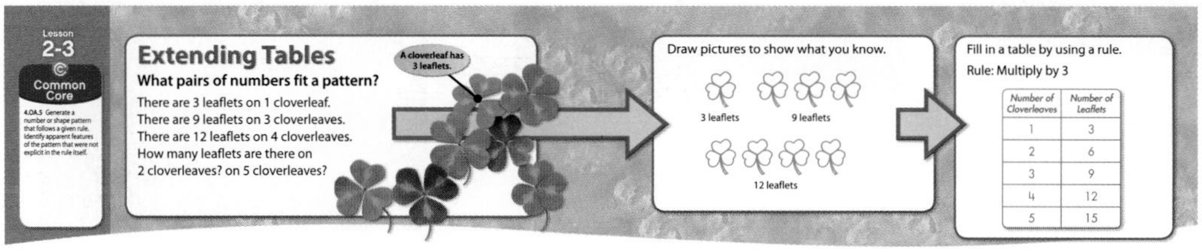

Grade 5 Visual Learning Bridge

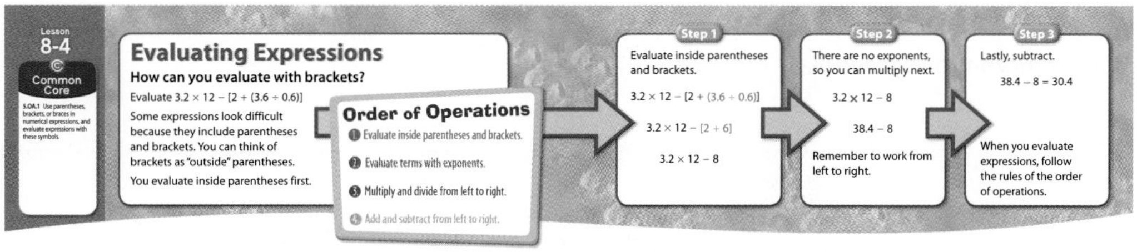

Grade 6 Visual Learning Bridge

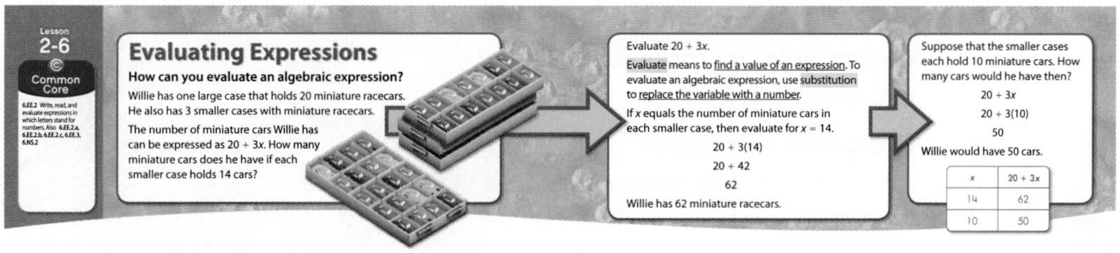

Patterns and Functions

- **Extending Repeating Patterns**
  Circle the shape that comes next.
  ○○□○○□○○□○○ | ○ □

- **Using Rules for Patterns**
  Use your rule to continue the pattern.
  38, 32, 26, 20, ▢, ▢

  Complete the table and find a rule.

d	12	14	20	26
$d +$ ▢	25	27	33	▢

Properties and Operations

- **Applying Properties**
  Write the sum. Change the order of the addends.
  $2 + 5 = \_\_\_$ $\qquad \_\_\_ + \_\_\_ = \_\_\_$

- **Using Inverse Operations**
  Find the number that makes both sentences true.
  ▢ $\times 6 = 42$ $\qquad 42 \div 6 =$ ▢

- **Using Order of Operations**
  Evaluate the expression.
  $27 \div (5 + 4) + 52$

Equations and Expressions

- **Finding Missing Numbers**
  $7 + 5 = 9 + \_\_\_$

- **Writing Expressions**
  Write an algebraic expression for the word phrase. Let x represent the number.
  four less than a number times six.

- **Solving Equations**
  $m + 41 = 95$

- **Listing Solution Pairs**
  Use the equation to complete the table.
  $b = \frac{a}{4} - 1$

a	4	8	10	12	16
b					

Equivalence: Equality/Inequality

- **Checking For Equivalence**
  Tell if the equation is true or false.
  $36 \div 4 = 3 \times 3 \times 3$

- **Comparing Quantities**
  Use >, <, or = for ○. $\qquad -8$ ○ -12

Frequent Progress Monitoring

enVisionMath Common Core provides frequent assessment opportunities as shown in the white boxes in the flowchart below.

Key

- **Student Edition**
- **Teacher's Edition**

Blackline Masters

- (A) Teacher Resource Masters
- (B) Math Diagnosis and Intervention System

Digital Resources

- (A) ExamView®
- (B) SuccessTracker

White Boxes = Assessment

Black Boxes = Intervention

At the start of the year →

- (A) Placement Test
- (B) Diagnostic Test
- (B) Diagnostic Test online
- (B) Intervention Lesson

At the start of a topic →

- Review What You Know
- (B) Topic Readiness Test online
- (B) Intervention Lesson

During a lesson →

- Do You Know How? Do You Understand?
- Explain It!
- Prevent Misconceptions
- Error Intervention (If... Then...)
- Reteaching Set

Response to Intervention (RTI)

enVisionMATH Common Core provides solid and effective intervention that makes it easy for teachers to respond to students' individual needs.

RTI Tier 1 Ongoing Intervention

Monitor Progress and prevent misconceptions during core lesson instruction.

Program features: Prevent Misconceptions, Error Intervention

Error Intervention

If students give incorrect products becau[...] the 4s facts,

then review the doubling strategy for 4s[...] 18 on the board and ask: *How can you u[...] product of 9 × 4?* [Double the product of [...] 18 = 36.] *Suppose that you want to multiply 6 × 4.* Write 6 × 4 on the board. *How can you use a 2s fact to find the product?* [You know 6 × 2 = 12, so double the product: 6 × 4 = 12 + 12 = 24.]

Preventing Misconceptions

Remind students that these methods of multiplying with 8 are strategies for helping to find the product. Point out that they are using facts they already know to help them with new facts.

RTI Tier 2 Strategic Intervention

Identify students' strengths and needs and provide appropriate support at the end of each lesson.

Program features:
Quick Check, Intervention Activities, Center Activities, Reteaching Masters

Math Diagnosis and Intervention System for end-of-topic assessment, reteaching, and enrichment

At the end of a lesson → At the end of a topic → Every four topics → At the end of the year

At the end of a lesson

- (A) Quick Check
- Intervention Activity
- (A) Reteaching Master
- Digital-resource reference

At the end of a topic

- Topic Test
- (A) Alternate Test
- (A) Performance Assessment
- (A) Topic Test from ExamView test generator
- (B) Intervention Lesson

Every four topics

- (A) Benchmark Test
- (B) Benchmark Test online
- (B) Intervention Lesson

At the end of the year

- (A) End-of-Year Test, Topics 1–16
- (A) End-of-Year Test from ExamView test generator
- (B) End-of-Year Test online
- (B) Intervention Lesson

Digital System

- Diagnose students' understanding of the Common Core State Standards automatically.
- Prescribe personalized instruction based on student performance.

RTI TIER 3 Intensive Intervention

Provide more intense personalized instruction for students who continue to struggle.

focusMATH

- Focus on foundational math skills—intensive, balanced and individualized
- Explicit instruction and stepped-out math models
- Each unit based on a specific NCTM focal point
- Systematic Assessment plans

Components Organized the Way You Teach

The **Teacher's Program Overview** includes a Content Guide and a Program Guide for your grade level.

The Topic Teacher's Editions are organized by Common Core Domains.

The **Teacher's Resource Masters** books are organized by Common Core Domain and contain the most frequently used Teacher Resource Masters.

Color-coded by Common Core Domains

- **Counting and Cardinality** (Grade K)
- **Operations and Algebraic Thinking** (Grades K–5)
- **Expressions and Equations** (Grade 6)
- **Number and Operations in Base Ten** (Grades K–5)
- **Number and Operations—Fractions** (Grades 3–5)
- **The Number System** (Grade 6)
- **Ratios and Proportional Relationships** (Grade 6)
- **Measurement and Data** (Grades K–5)
- **Statistics and Probability** (Grade 6)
- **Geometry** (Grades K–6)

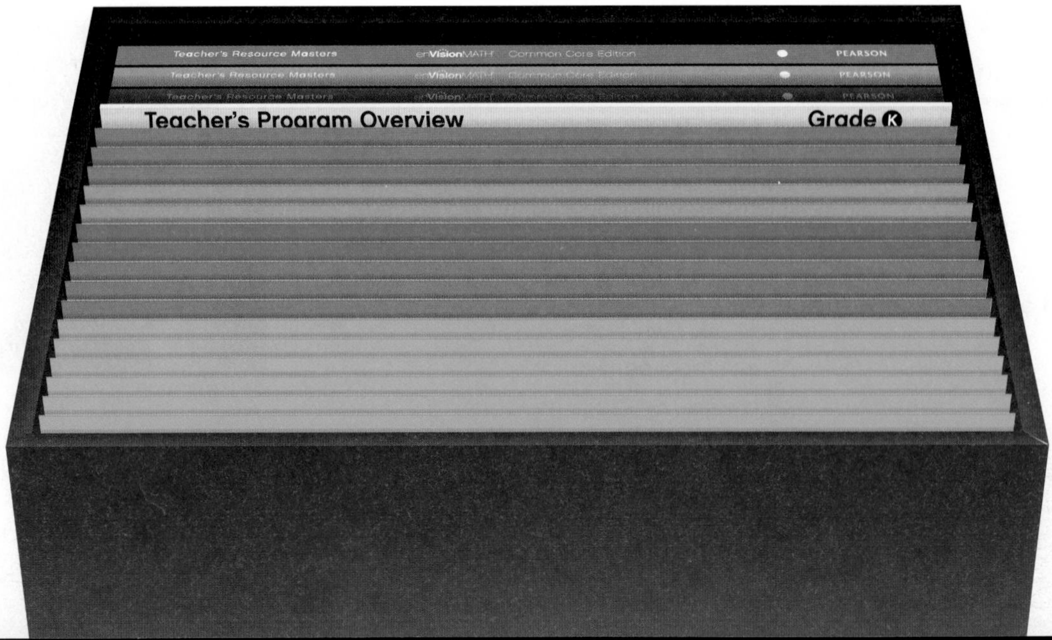

Student Edition

Common Core Reteaching and Practice Workbook

Instruction for All Learners

Ready-Made Center for Differentiated Instruction

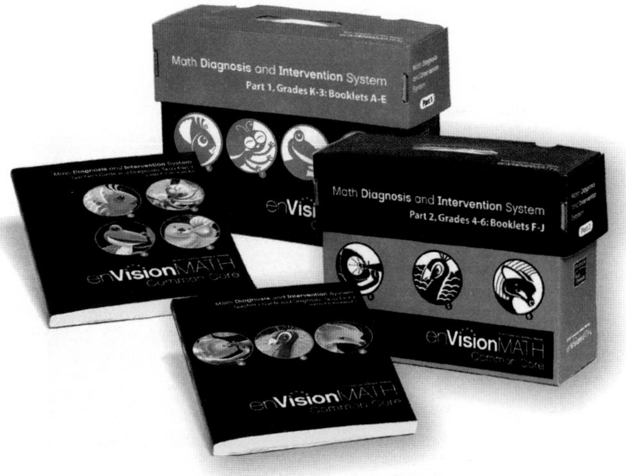

Math Diagnosis and Intervention System

focusMATH

Math Literature

Interactive Math Stories Big Book
(Grades K–2)

Math Library

Hands-On Materials

Manipulative Kits

- Classroom Kits
- Overhead Kits
- Student Kits
- Center Activities Kit
- Magnetic Kits (Grades K–2)

Comprehensive Digital Resources Online and on CD-ROM

eText

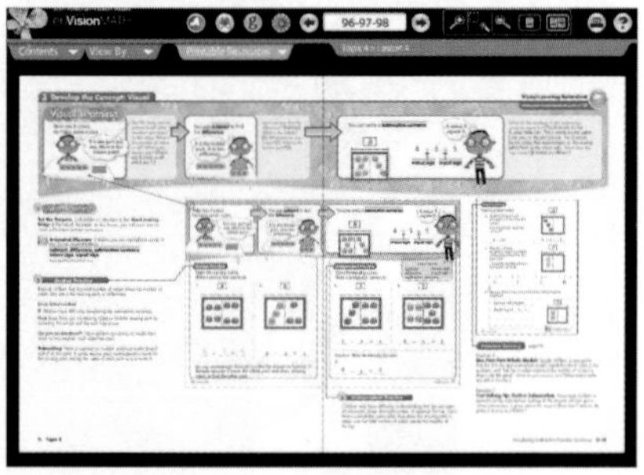

The **Teacher's Edition** allows you to plan your math lessons from home or school. Available online and on CD-ROM.

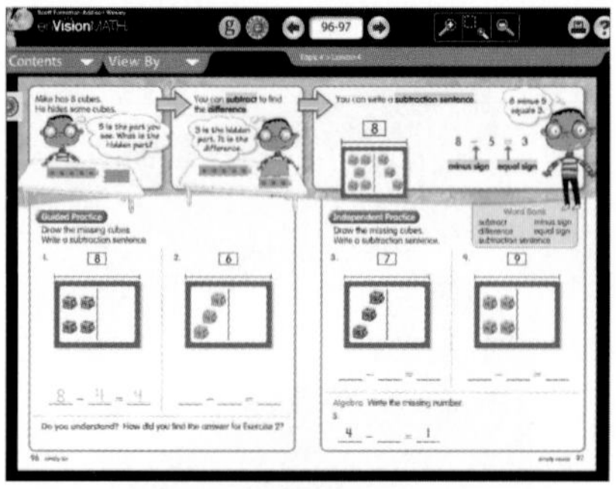

The **Student Edition** includes the complete student edition along with interactive tools and frequently used Teacher Resource Masters. Available online only.

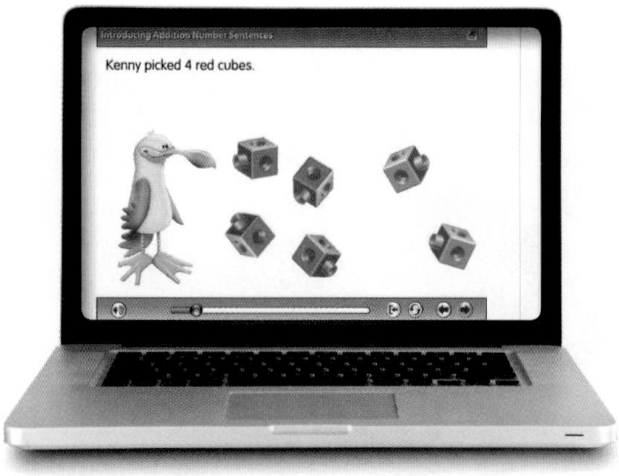

Instructional Resources

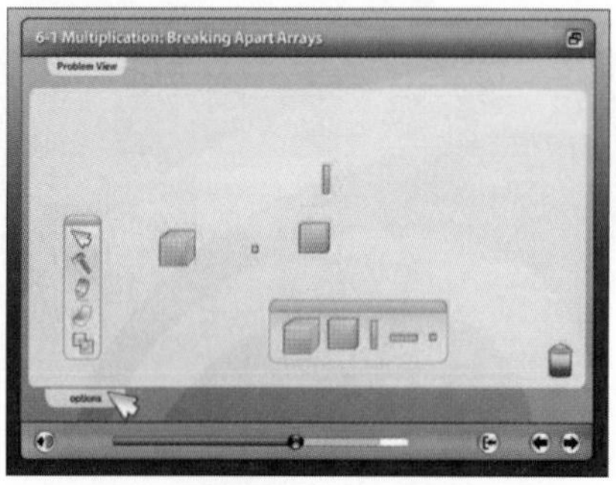

The **Tools4Math** are virtual manipulatives that let students explore and visualize concepts. Available online only.

The **Animated Interactive Math Stories (K–2)** introduce new content and engage young learners with animations that bring new math concepts to life. Available online only.

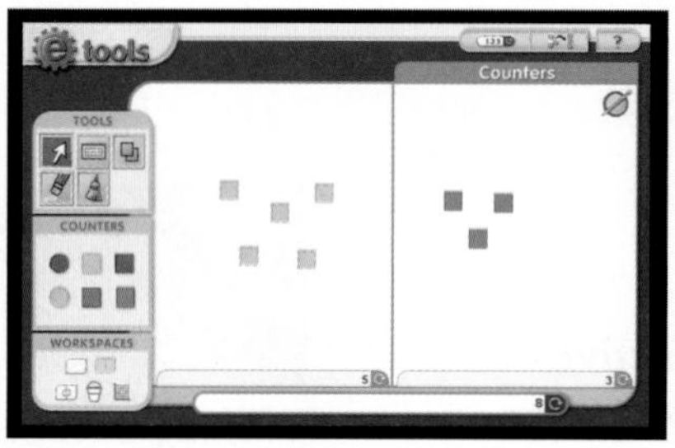

The **eTools** actively involve students with digital manipulatives that clearly demonstrate concepts. Available online only.

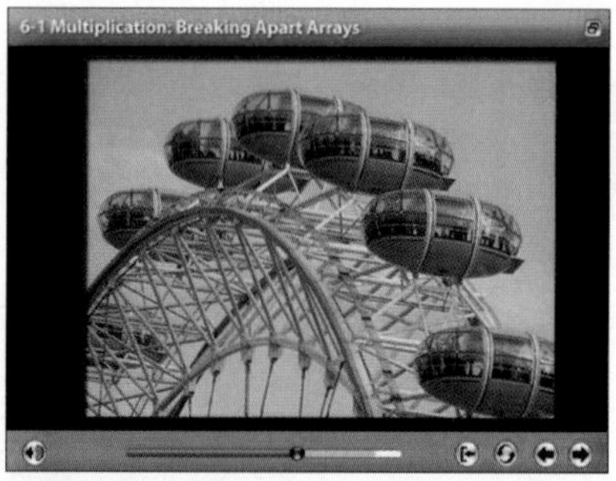

The **Topic Opener Videos (3–6)** introduce new content with compelling, real-world video segments. Available online only.

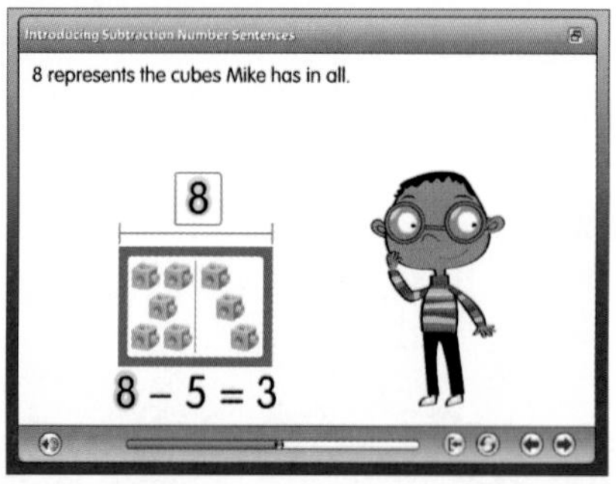

The **Visual Learning Animations** transform teaching and learning with animations that let students hear, see, and learn math concepts. Available online and on CD-ROM.

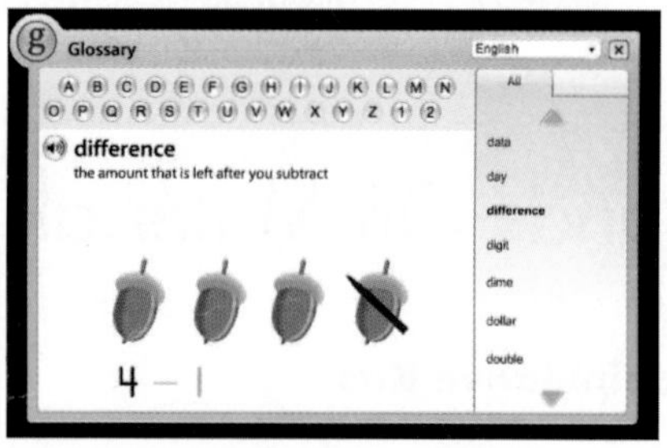

The **Animated Glossary** provides definitions and animations for new math vocabulary. Available online only.

Professional Development

On Site Professional Development

Pearson Professional Development services help you effectively implement Common Core State Standards.

Workshops include ...

- ***enVisionMATH* Common Core**
  An introduction to the Common Core
- **Implementing *enVisionMATH* Common Core**
  Compare differences from former standards

Plus these general sessions:

- **Leading the Way for Successful Common Core Implementation in Mathematics K–12**
  A general workshop on the Common Core
- **Classroom Assessment for Student Learning**
  Assessment practices for the Common Core

MyPearsonTraining.com

Online Professional Development

Learn more about the Common Core! Watch online video and tutorials 24/7 and participate in live, Web-based sessions with expert trainers.

Ask your Pearson representative for details.

Teacher Resources

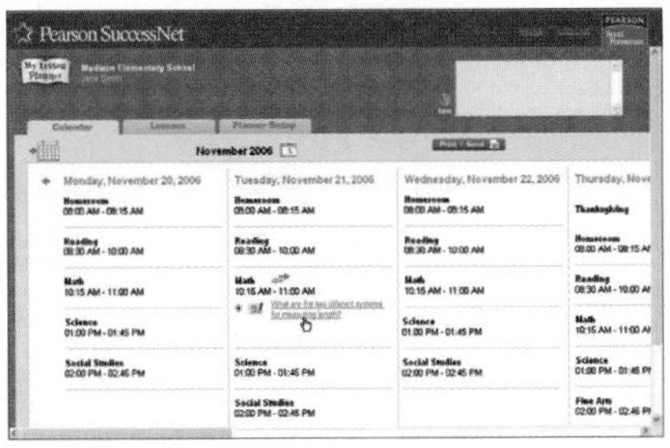

The **Online Lesson Planner** helps you organize your lesson plans by day, week, and month. Available online.

Build a Lesson Suite assists you as you create personalized lessons in the best sequence for your students. Available online.

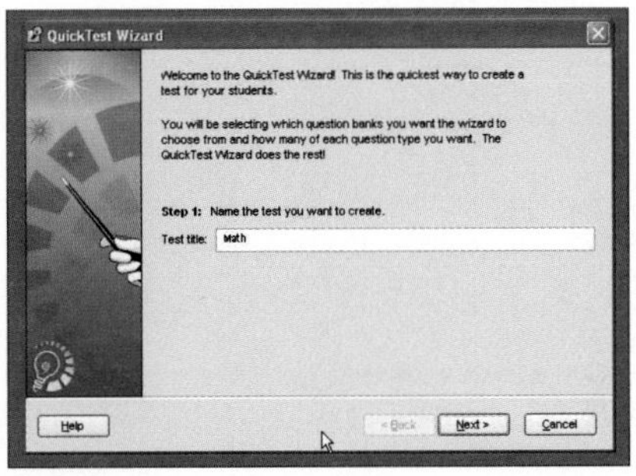

Examview® Assessment Suite allows you to customize tests to your state standards. Available on CD-ROM.

Math Background

Research says that the quality of instruction depends on the teacher's knowledge of math content (Kilpatrick, 2001).

enVisionMATH Common Core provides:

- **Math Background** for teachers in every Topic Teacher's Edition
- **Math Background for Teachers** in every lesson

STEM Education

STEM or, Science, Technology, Engineering, and Mathematics, Education has as its goal increasing the number of college students choosing majoring in science or technology-related fields. STEM Education encourages a curriculum that is built around the active engagement of students in problem solving. *enVisionMATH Common Core* offers students opportunities to use mathematics to solve real-life problems in science. These opportunities are highlighted with a STEM icon that reminds students that the problem they are working on is related to science, engineering, or technology.

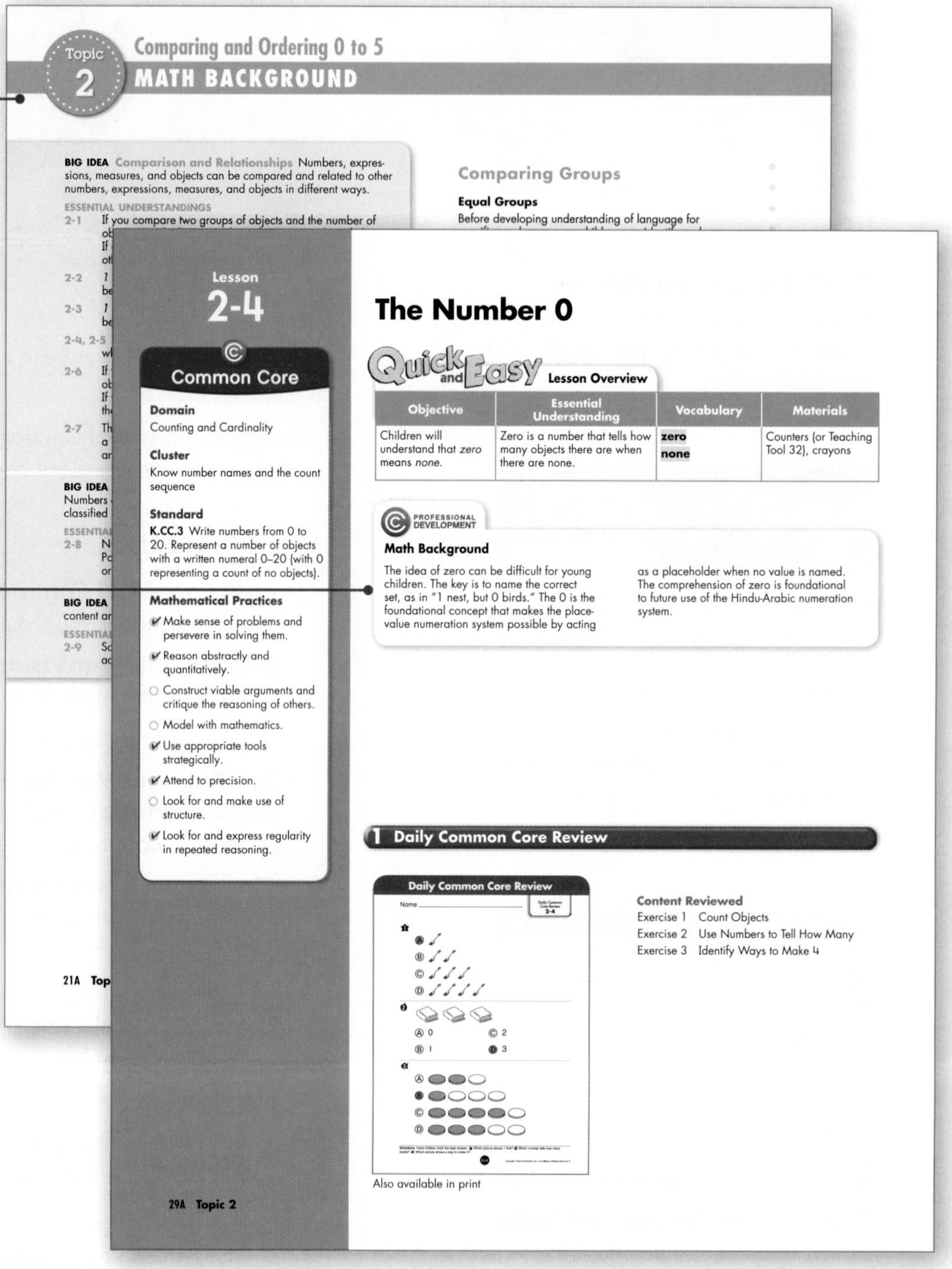
Topic 2 Comparing and Ordering 0 to 5
MATH BACKGROUND

BIG IDEA Comparison and Relationships Numbers, expressions, measures, and objects can be compared and related to other numbers, expressions, measures, and objects in different ways.

Comparing Groups
Equal Groups

Lesson 2-4

The Number 0

Quick and Easy Lesson Overview

Objective	Essential Understanding	Vocabulary	Materials
Children will understand that *zero* means *none*.	Zero is a number that tells how many objects there are when there are none.	zero none	Counters (or Teaching Tool 32), crayons

Common Core

Domain
Counting and Cardinality

Cluster
Know number names and the count sequence

Standard
K.CC.3 Write numbers from 0 to 20. Represent a number of objects with a written numeral 0–20 (with 0 representing a count of no objects).

Mathematical Practices
- ✔ Make sense of problems and persevere in solving them.
- ✔ Reason abstractly and quantitatively.
- ○ Construct viable arguments and critique the reasoning of others.
- ○ Model with mathematics.
- ✔ Use appropriate tools strategically.
- ✔ Attend to precision.
- ○ Look for and make use of structure.
- ✔ Look for and express regularity in repeated reasoning.

PROFESSIONAL DEVELOPMENT

Math Background
The idea of zero can be difficult for young children. The key is to name the correct set, as in "1 nest, but 0 birds." The 0 is the foundational concept that makes the place-value numeration system possible by acting as a placeholder when no value is named. The comprehension of zero is foundational to future use of the Hindu-Arabic numeration system.

1 Daily Common Core Review

Content Reviewed
Exercise 1 Count Objects
Exercise 2 Use Numbers to Tell How Many
Exercise 3 Identify Ways to Make 4

Also available in print

29A Topic 2

▲ **Teacher's Edition**

Development Tools

by Skip Fennell

> *Together they can be valuable professional development tools, helping teachers, math leaders, and others unpack key mathematics topics within and across grade levels.*

As you begin the multi-year transition toward full implementation and assessment of the Common Core State Standards (CCSS), you will have two related opportunities for support. These are the **Progressions Documents** and the proposed products of the **Illustrative Mathematics Project.**

The **Progressions Documents** for the CCSS are a collection of narratives, generally organized around the mathematics content domains of the CCSS (e.g., Number and Operations in Base Ten). These documents trace the learning progression, across grade levels, of a particular domain or one key element of a domain. Each narrative is informed by research on learning, the logical structure of the mathematics being presented, and best practice. Together they can be valuable professional development tools, helping teachers, math leaders, and others unpack key mathematics topics within and across grade levels. The Progressions Documents, through their examination of sequence and topic emphasis within a particular domain, should help drive discussion and facilitate decisions related to the amount of time needed for particular topics, the best use of instructional tools, the influence of various mathematical practices, and other transition-related issues.

The Progressions Documents also have the potential to validate or suggest research in mathematics education. Research into the progressions can raise questions and issues that may impact the standards revision process as well as frame further research questions. Work on the Progressions Documents is supported by the Brookhill Foundation. Final documents will be available on the University of Arizona's Institute for Mathematics and Education website.

The intent of the **Illustrative Mathematics Project** is to provide guidance to states, schools, school districts, assessment consortia, testing companies, and curriculum developers by providing sample tasks to illustrate the range and type of mathematics activities that students will experience in classrooms where the CCSS are being implemented and assessed. The web-based Illustrative Mathematics Project will include a process for the submission, discussion, review, and publication of relevant learning activities or tasks. This work is being supported by the Bill and Melinda Gates Foundation; the project's site can be found through the University of Arizona's Institute for Mathematics and Education.

The Common Core State Standards insist that all students must be supported in their learning so they can meet all of the standards. Differentiating instruction helps students achieve this goal.

Meeting Individual Needs

enVisionMATH Common Core provides support for:

English Language Learners (ELL)

- **For each topic** the Meeting Individual Needs feature provides topic-specific ELL considerations plus an ELL activity.
- Each lesson's **Problem-Based Interactive Learning** activity uses instructional strategies that help all students but are especially helpful to ELL students.
- ELL strategies are also provided at the end of the lesson.
- The pictorial nature of the **Visual Learning Bridge** in each lesson also helps ELL students.

Special Needs

- **For each topic** the Meeting Individual Needs feature provides topic-specific considerations for special education students plus an activity.
- **For each lesson** the **Visual Learning Bridge** helps special education students focus on one idea at a time.

Below Level

- **For each topic** the Meeting Individual Needs feature provides topic-specific considerations for below-level students plus an activity.
- **For each lesson** the program provides an Intervention Activity, a Reteaching Master, a reference to a digital resource appropriate for below-level students, and an Intervention Lesson in the Math Diagnosis and Intervention System.

Advanced/Gifted

- **For each topic** the Meeting Individual Needs feature provides topic-specific considerations for advanced/gifted learners plus an activity.
- **For each lesson** the program provides an Advanced Center Activity, an Enrichment Master, and a reference to a digital resource appropriate for advanced students.

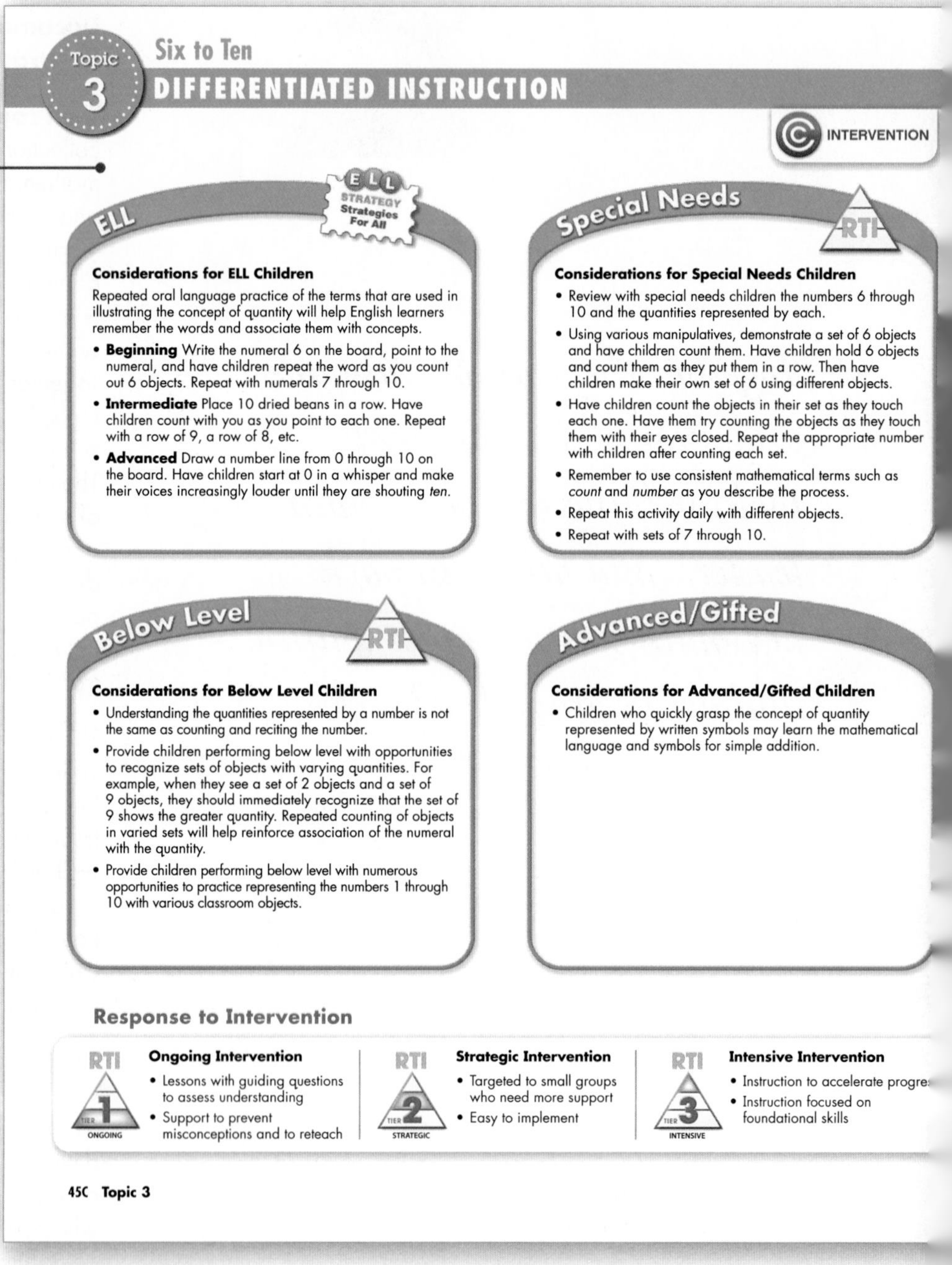

Topic 3 Six to Ten

DIFFERENTIATED INSTRUCTION

INTERVENTION

ELL

ELL STRATEGY Strategies For All

Considerations for ELL Children

Repeated oral language practice of the terms that are used in illustrating the concept of quantity will help English learners remember the words and associate them with concepts.

- **Beginning** Write the numeral 6 on the board, point to the numeral, and have children repeat the word as you count out 6 objects. Repeat with numerals 7 through 10.
- **Intermediate** Place 10 dried beans in a row. Have children count with you as you point to each one. Repeat with a row of 9, a row of 8, etc.
- **Advanced** Draw a number line from 0 through 10 on the board. Have children start at 0 in a whisper and make their voices increasingly louder until they are shouting *ten*.

Special Needs

RTI

Considerations for Special Needs Children

- Review with special needs children the numbers 6 through 10 and the quantities represented by each.
- Using various manipulatives, demonstrate a set of 6 objects and have children count them. Have children hold 6 objects and count them as they put them in a row. Then have children make their own set of 6 using different objects.
- Have children count the objects in their set as they touch each one. Have them try counting the objects as they touch them with their eyes closed. Repeat the appropriate number with children after counting each set.
- Remember to use consistent mathematical terms such as *count* and *number* as you describe the process.
- Repeat this activity daily with different objects.
- Repeat with sets of 7 through 10.

Below Level

RTI

Considerations for Below Level Children

- Understanding the quantities represented by a number is not the same as counting and reciting the number.
- Provide children performing below level with opportunities to recognize sets of objects with varying quantities. For example, when they see a set of 2 objects and a set of 9 objects, they should immediately recognize that the set of 9 shows the greater quantity. Repeated counting of objects in varied sets will help reinforce association of the numeral with the quantity.
- Provide children performing below level with numerous opportunities to practice representing the numbers 1 through 10 with various classroom objects.

Advanced/Gifted

Considerations for Advanced/Gifted Children

- Children who quickly grasp the concept of quantity represented by written symbols may learn the mathematical language and symbols for simple addition.

Response to Intervention

RTI TIER 1 ONGOING **Ongoing Intervention**

- Lessons with guiding questions to assess understanding
- Support to prevent misconceptions and to reteach

RTI TIER 2 STRATEGIC **Strategic Intervention**

- Targeted to small groups who need more support
- Easy to implement

RTI TIER 3 INTENSIVE **Intensive Intervention**

- Instruction to accelerate progre
- Instruction focused on foundational skills

45C Topic 3

▲ **Teacher's Edition**

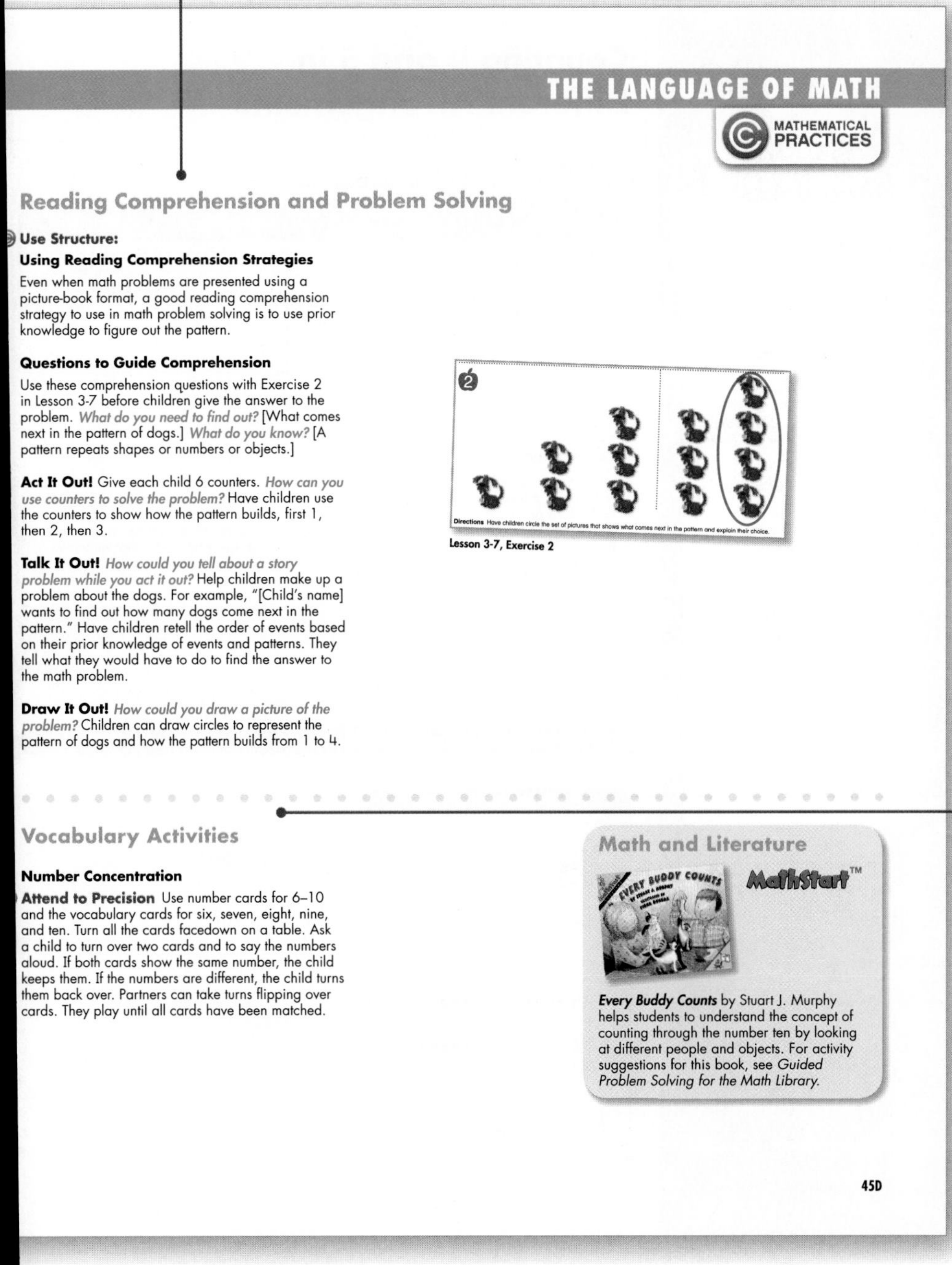

THE LANGUAGE OF MATH

MATHEMATICAL PRACTICES

Reading Comprehension and Problem Solving

Use Structure:

Using Reading Comprehension Strategies

Even when math problems are presented using a picture-book format, a good reading comprehension strategy to use in math problem solving is to use prior knowledge to figure out the pattern.

Questions to Guide Comprehension

Use these comprehension questions with Exercise 2 in Lesson 3-7 before children give the answer to the problem. *What do you need to find out?* [What comes next in the pattern of dogs.] *What do you know?* [A pattern repeats shapes or numbers or objects.]

Act It Out! Give each child 6 counters. *How can you use counters to solve the problem?* Have children use the counters to show how the pattern builds, first 1, then 2, then 3.

Talk It Out! *How could you tell about a story problem while you act it out?* Help children make up a problem about the dogs. For example, "[Child's name] wants to find out how many dogs come next in the pattern." Have children retell the order of events based on their prior knowledge of events and patterns. They tell what they would have to do to find the answer to the math problem.

Draw It Out! *How could you draw a picture of the problem?* Children can draw circles to represent the pattern of dogs and how the pattern builds from 1 to 4.

2

Directions Have children circle the set of pictures that shows what comes next in the pattern and explain their choice.

Lesson 3-7, Exercise 2

Vocabulary Activities

Number Concentration

Attend to Precision Use number cards for 6–10 and the vocabulary cards for six, seven, eight, nine, and ten. Turn all the cards facedown on a table. Ask a child to turn over two cards and to say the numbers aloud. If both cards show the same number, the child keeps them. If the numbers are different, the child turns them back over. Partners can take turns flipping over cards. They play until all cards have been matched.

Math and Literature

MathStart™

Every Buddy Counts by Stuart J. Murphy helps students to understand the concept of counting through the number ten by looking at different people and objects. For activity suggestions for this book, see *Guided Problem Solving for the Math Library.*

45D

Reading Comprehension and Problem Solving

Research says reading comprehension plays an important role in understanding word problems in math (Mayer and Wittrock, 1996).

enVisionMATH Common Core provides:

- **Reading comprehension** strategies at the start of each topic along with questions to guide comprehension using a Problem-Solving Recording Sheet.

Vocabulary

Research says mathematics is like a language and some techniques used to learn language can be used to learn the language of math (Paris and Cunningham, 1996).

enVisionMATH Common Core provides:

- **Vocabulary Cards** in the Teacher's Resource Masters that have words on one side and definitions on the other.
- **Vocabulary Activities** in front of each topic that help students solidify their understanding of math terms.
- **Vocabulary** in lesson notes in the Teacher's Edition.

Essential Understanding

The **Essential Understanding** describes the mathematics students **will understand** related to the Common Core Standards.

STATE STANDARDS

All Common Core State Standards information is listed at point of use in every lesson for easy reference. Domains, Clusters, Standards, and Mathematical Practices are identified for every lesson.

PROFESSIONAL DEVELOPMENT

Built-in **Professional Development** focuses on Mathematical Practices.

Daily Review

The **Daily Common Core Review** helps you reinforce Common Core State Standards.

Lesson 1-5

Common Core

Domain
Counting and Cardinality

Cluster
Count to tell the number of objects.

Standards
K.CC.4.b Understand that the last number name said tells the number of objects counted. The number of objects is the same regardless of their arrangement or the order in which they were counted. Also **K.CC.5**

Mathematical Practices
- ✔ Make sense of problems and persevere in solving them.
- ✔ Reason abstractly and quantitatively.
- ○ Construct viable arguments and critique the reasoning of others.
- ✔ Model with mathematics.
- ✔ Use appropriate tools strategically.
- ✔ Attend to precision.
- ✔ Look for and make use of structure.
- ○ Look for and express regularity in repeated reasoning.

Counting 4 and 5 in Different Arrangements

Quick and Easy Lesson Overview

Objective	Essential Understanding	Vocabulary	Materials
Children will identify whether a particular set includes 4 or 5 objects.	Counting tells how many are in a set, regardless of their arrangement or the order in which they were counted. The last number said when counting a set is the total. Counting is cumulative.		Counters (or Teaching Tool 32), sticky dots

PROFESSIONAL DEVELOPMENT

Math Background

Subitizing, or instantly recognizing collections up to 5 after a brief view, is an important skill for the early grades. It is easiest for children to recognize the number of objects when they are placed in a row, a column, or in a diagonal line. Recognizing the number is more difficult when the objects are scattered randomly, however. Subitizing helps children solve problems that involve counting, addition, and subtraction. This lesson gives children practice in instantly recognizing collections of 4 and 5, and emphasizes that the same number of objects can be arranged in various ways.

1 Daily Common Core Review

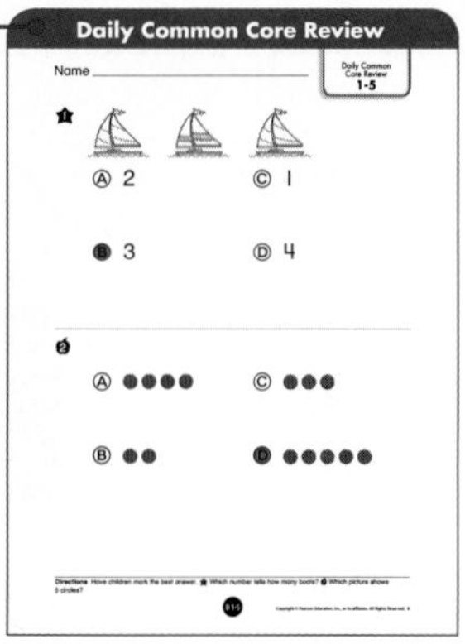

Also available in print

Content Reviewed
Exercise 1 Use Numbers to Tell How Many
Exercise 2 Count 5

11A Topic 1

▲ **Teacher's Edition**

Problem-Based Interactive Learning

enVisionMATH Common Core provides Problem-Based Interactive Learning opportunities for effective concept development. Each Problem-Based Interactive Learning experience has four instructional phases.

- **Engage Students.**

  Set the Purpose of the activity. Then ask and discuss the Connect question to help students recall prior knowledge.

- **Students Solve and Discuss a Problem.**

  Pose the Problem. Have students work together to solve the problems as the teacher facilitates (observes, asks questions, etc.).

  Have students share their thinking and work. When possible, show more than one solution.

- **Make the Important Math Explicit.**

  For a classroom conversation use the questions and ideas that follow **Pose the Problem.**

- **Deepen Understanding.**

  Extend. As time permits, provide the problem extension to increase knowledge and depth of understanding.

MATHEMATICAL PRACTICES

Observe **Mathematical Practices** during Problem-Based Interactive Learning.

---

2 Develop the Concept: Interactive — MATHEMATICAL PRACTICES

10–15 min

Problem-Based Interactive Learning

Hands-On Minds-On

Overview Children will understand that the number of objects in a set is the same regardless of their arrangement. They will also be able to recognize arrangements of 4 or 5 objects both with and without counting.

Focus How can you recognize different arrangements of 4 or 5 objects?

Materials Counters (or Teaching Tool 32), 9 sticky dots per child

Engage

Set the Purpose Remind children that they have counted to 4 and 5. Remind children that there is more than one way to arrange 4 objects or 5 objects. *Let's look at different ways of arranging 4 counters and 5 counters.*

Connect *Turn to a partner. Say "Give me five!"* Children should slap hands with a friend. *Why do you say "Give me five!" instead of "Give me two!" or "Give me three!"?* [Because you are slapping five fingers.] *Hold up all five fingers on one hand. Can you use both hands to show five fingers in a different way? Is there another way? Does each way still show five fingers?* [Yes] Help children demonstrate that they still have five fingers showing by having them touch each finger to their chin one at a time.

MATHEMATICAL PRACTICES

Reason Abstractly Look for and correct the misconception that the arrangement affects the total number of bees in the hive.

Pose the Problem *The beekeeper has two hives full of bees. He needs to count how many bees are in each hive, but they keep moving.*

Model *Look at the beehive hanging from the tree. I'll put four counters in the beehive. They'll represent the four bees that are in the hive.* Place four counters in the hive in a diagonal pattern and have children do the same. *How many bees are in the hive?* [4] *How do you know?* [We put in four counters so there are four bees.] Move the four counters around inside the hive and ask children to do the same. *How many bees are there now? How do you know?* [4; the counters moved but the number of bees stayed the same.] *How could you check your answer to be sure there are 4 bees?* [I could count the counters. If the last number I say is four, I have the correct answer.] Have children look at the boxes on the left side of the student page. *Now let's color boxes to show how many bees are in the hive. How many boxes will we color?* [4]

Use Repetition Repeat the same modeled activity using five counters instead of four.

Small-Group Interaction Have children remove the counters from their hives. Have Partner A place either 4 or 5 counters in the first hive, count how many, and announce the number. Then have that child move the counters so they are in a different arrangement. Partner B then counts to check that the number of counters is the same. Have children switch roles and repeat the activity.

Use Drawings Distribute 9 sticky dots to each child. Ask children to place four dots in one hive and five in the other hive. A variety of arrangements should be encouraged. Children can then add wings and other details to the bees. As children work, ask *How many bees are in the hive?*

Extend *Use your words and no actions to describe an arrangement of 5 counters. Ask your partner to make an arrangement that matches your description.* [Answers will vary.]

DIGITAL eTools **Counters** www.pearsonsuccessnet.com

11

Visual Learning

Step-by-step **Visual Instruction** makes the math explicit for students and parents.

- **Visual concept development** that helps students access math skills and concepts by seeing ideas developed in visual displays.
- **Visual Learning Bridge** which is a pictorial, step-by-step bridge between the Problem-Based Interactive Learning activity and the lesson exercises. It helps students focus on one idea at a time as well as see connections within a sequence of ideas. This is especially helpful for visual learners and English language learners.
- **Guiding questions** in blue type that help you guide students through the examples and give you an opportunity to check students' understanding.
- **Pictures with a purpose** throughout the lessons that show representations of math concepts and show data for math problems in real-world contexts.

MATHEMATICAL PRACTICES

During **Guided Practice**, students are explaining, writing, and creating their own problems.

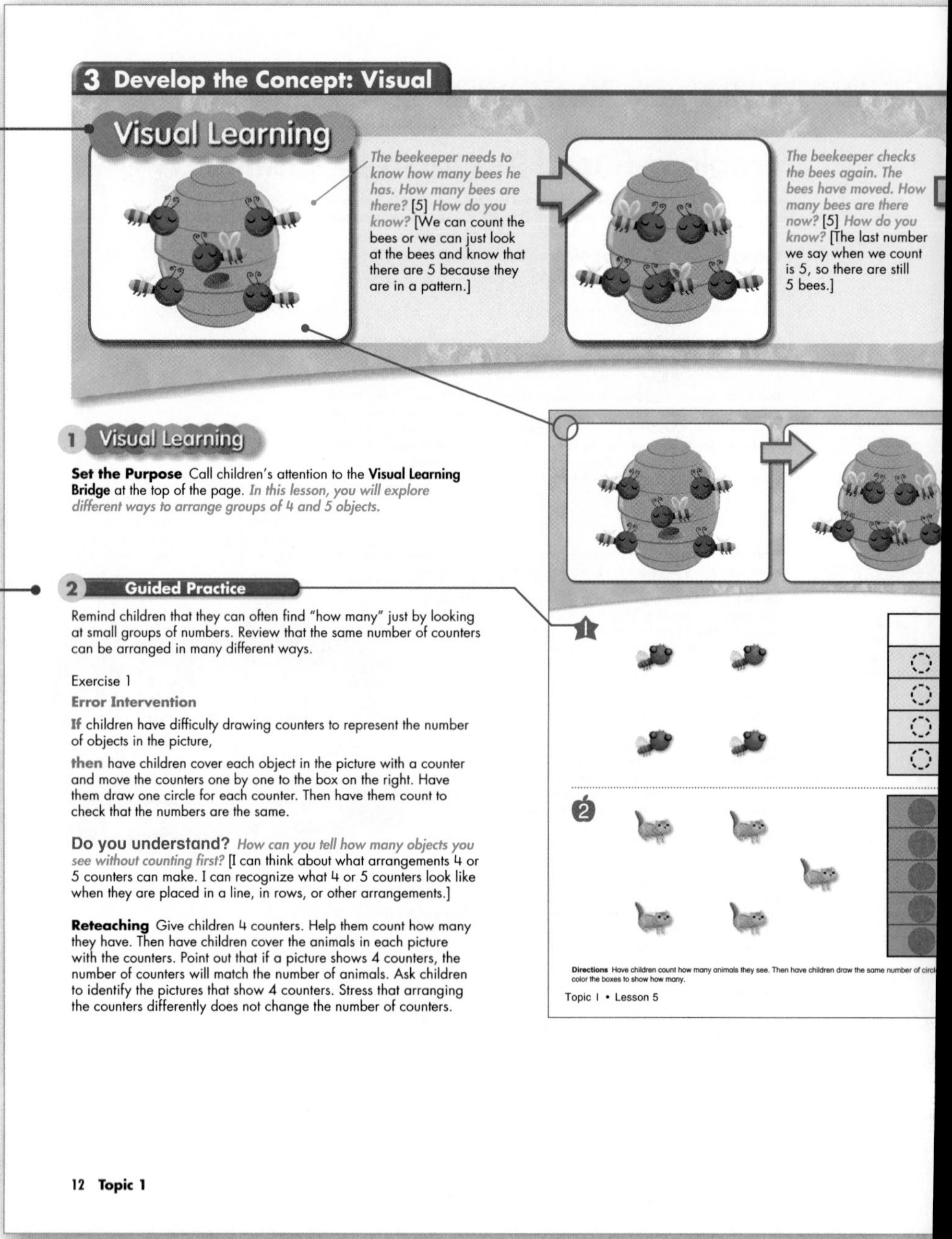

3 Develop the Concept: Visual

Visual Learning

The beekeeper needs to know how many bees he has. How many bees are there? [5] *How do you know?* [We can count the bees or we can just look at the bees and know that there are 5 because they are in a pattern.]

The beekeeper checks the bees again. The bees have moved. How many bees are there now? [5] *How do you know?* [The last number we say when we count is 5, so there are still 5 bees.]

1 Visual Learning

Set the Purpose Call children's attention to the **Visual Learning Bridge** at the top of the page. *In this lesson, you will explore different ways to arrange groups of 4 and 5 objects.*

2 Guided Practice

Remind children that they can often find "how many" just by looking at small groups of numbers. Review that the same number of counters can be arranged in many different ways.

Exercise 1

Error Intervention

If children have difficulty drawing counters to represent the number of objects in the picture,

then have children cover each object in the picture with a counter and move the counters one by one to the box on the right. Have them draw one circle for each counter. Then have them count to check that the numbers are the same.

Do you understand? *How can you tell how many objects you see without counting first?* [I can think about what arrangements 4 or 5 counters can make. I can recognize what 4 or 5 counters look like when they are placed in a line, in rows, or other arrangements.]

Reteaching Give children 4 counters. Help them count how many they have. Then have children cover the animals in each picture with the counters. Point out that if a picture shows 4 counters, the number of counters will match the number of animals. Ask children to identify the pictures that show 4 counters. Stress that arranging the counters differently does not change the number of counters.

Directions Have children count how many animals they see. Then have children draw the same number of circl... color the boxes to show how many.

Topic 1 • Lesson 5

12 **Topic 1**

▲ **Teacher's Edition**

Visual Learning Animations

Visual Learning Animations can be used to present the Visual Learning Bridge digitally with animation. The content of each student lesson comes alive in the Visual Learning Animations. These animations provide additional questions and promote deeper understanding of concepts.

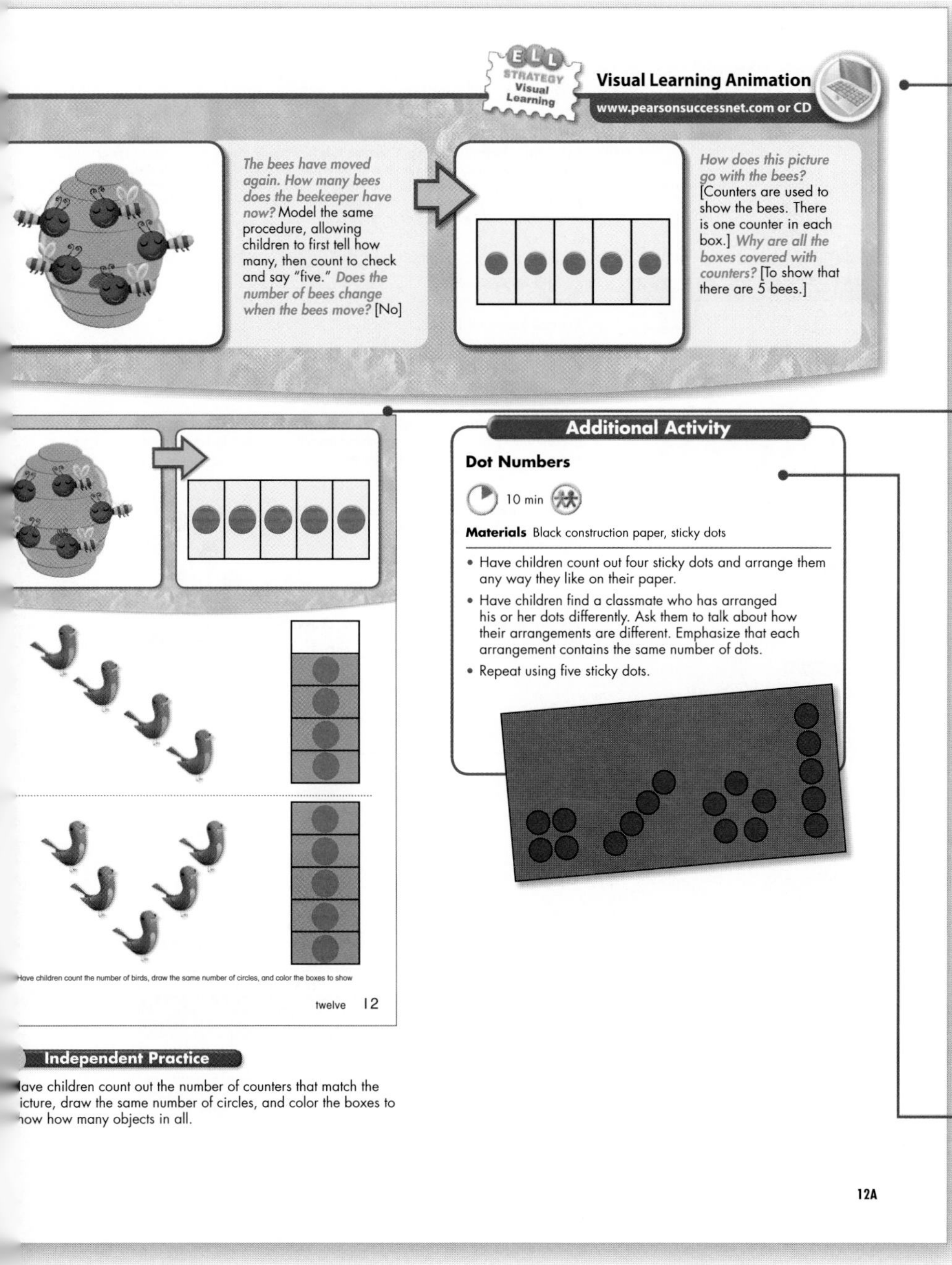
ELL STRATEGY Visual Learning

Visual Learning Animation

www.pearsonsuccessnet.com or CD

The bees have moved again. How many bees does the beekeeper have now? Model the same procedure, allowing children to first tell how many, then count to check and say "five." *Does the number of bees change when the bees move?* [No]

How does this picture go with the bees? [Counters are used to show the bees. There is one counter in each box.] *Why are all the boxes covered with counters?* [To show that there are 5 bees.]

Additional Activity

Dot Numbers

10 min

Materials Black construction paper, sticky dots

- Have children count out four sticky dots and arrange them any way they like on their paper.
- Have children find a classmate who has arranged his or her dots differently. Ask them to talk about how their arrangements are different. Emphasize that each arrangement contains the same number of dots.
- Repeat using five sticky dots.

Have children count the number of birds, draw the same number of circles, and color the boxes to show

twelve 12

Independent Practice

Have children count out the number of counters that match the picture, draw the same number of circles, and color the boxes to show how many objects in all.

12A

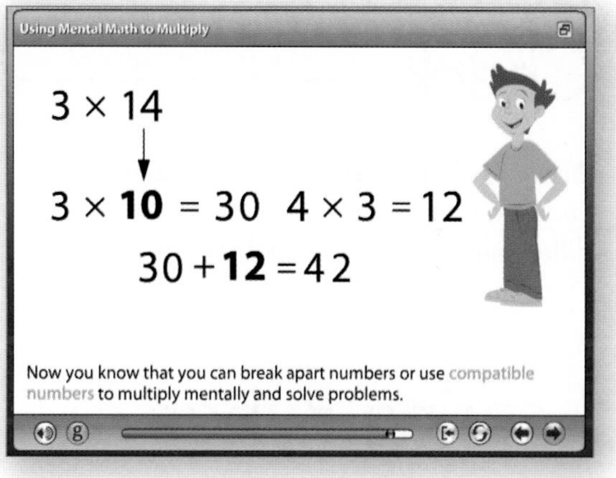

Visual Learning Bridge

A **Visual Learning Bridge** is shown at the start of the lesson in the Student Edition and also appears in the Teacher's Edition along with guiding questions in blue type.

MATHEMATICAL PRACTICES

Problem-solving exercises apply Mathematical Practices and higher-order thinking.

Assessment and Prescription

Assess understanding, differentiate instruction, and observe the 8 Mathematical Practices in action with teacher-guided and independent-leveled Center Activities.

Daily Quick Check

Daily Quick Check assesses student understanding with an eye toward differentiation for individual student needs.

Scoring Rubric

Scoring Rubric includes three levels of performance and samples of student work.

Prescription

Prescription is provided for Differentiated Instruction.

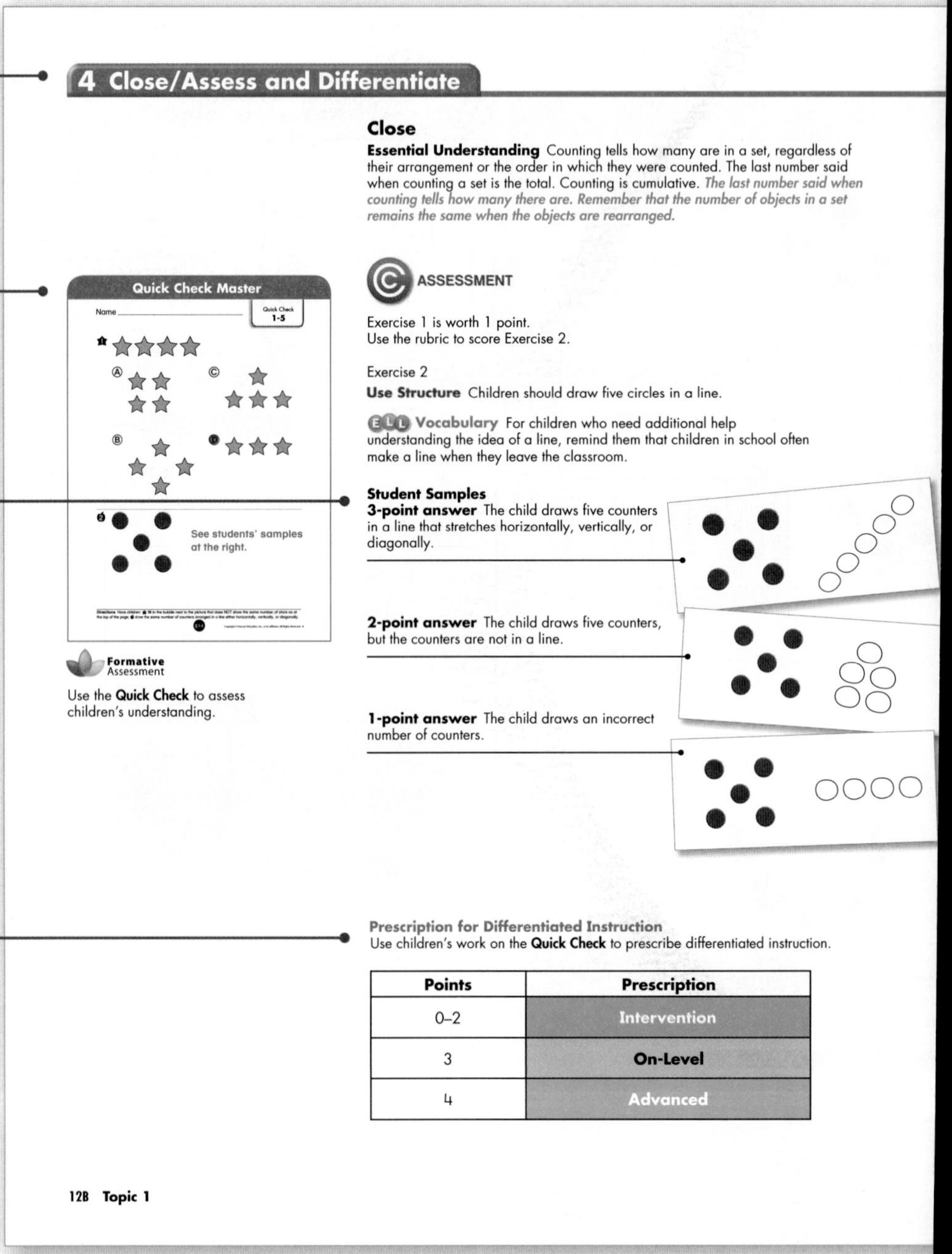

4 Close/Assess and Differentiate

Close

Essential Understanding Counting tells how many are in a set, regardless of their arrangement or the order in which they were counted. The last number said when counting a set is the total. Counting is cumulative. *The last number said when counting tells how many there are. Remember that the number of objects in a set remains the same when the objects are rearranged.*

Quick Check Master

Name

Quick Check 1-5

See students' samples at the right.

Formative Assessment

Use the **Quick Check** to assess children's understanding.

ASSESSMENT

Exercise 1 is worth 1 point.
Use the rubric to score Exercise 2.

Exercise 2
Use Structure Children should draw five circles in a line.

ELL Vocabulary For children who need additional help understanding the idea of a line, remind them that children in school often make a line when they leave the classroom.

Student Samples
3-point answer The child draws five counters in a line that stretches horizontally, vertically, or diagonally.

2-point answer The child draws five counters, but the counters are not in a line.

1-point answer The child draws an incorrect number of counters.

Prescription for Differentiated Instruction
Use children's work on the **Quick Check** to prescribe differentiated instruction.

Points	Prescription
0–2	Intervention
3	On-Level
4	Advanced

12B Topic 1

▲ **Teacher's Edition**

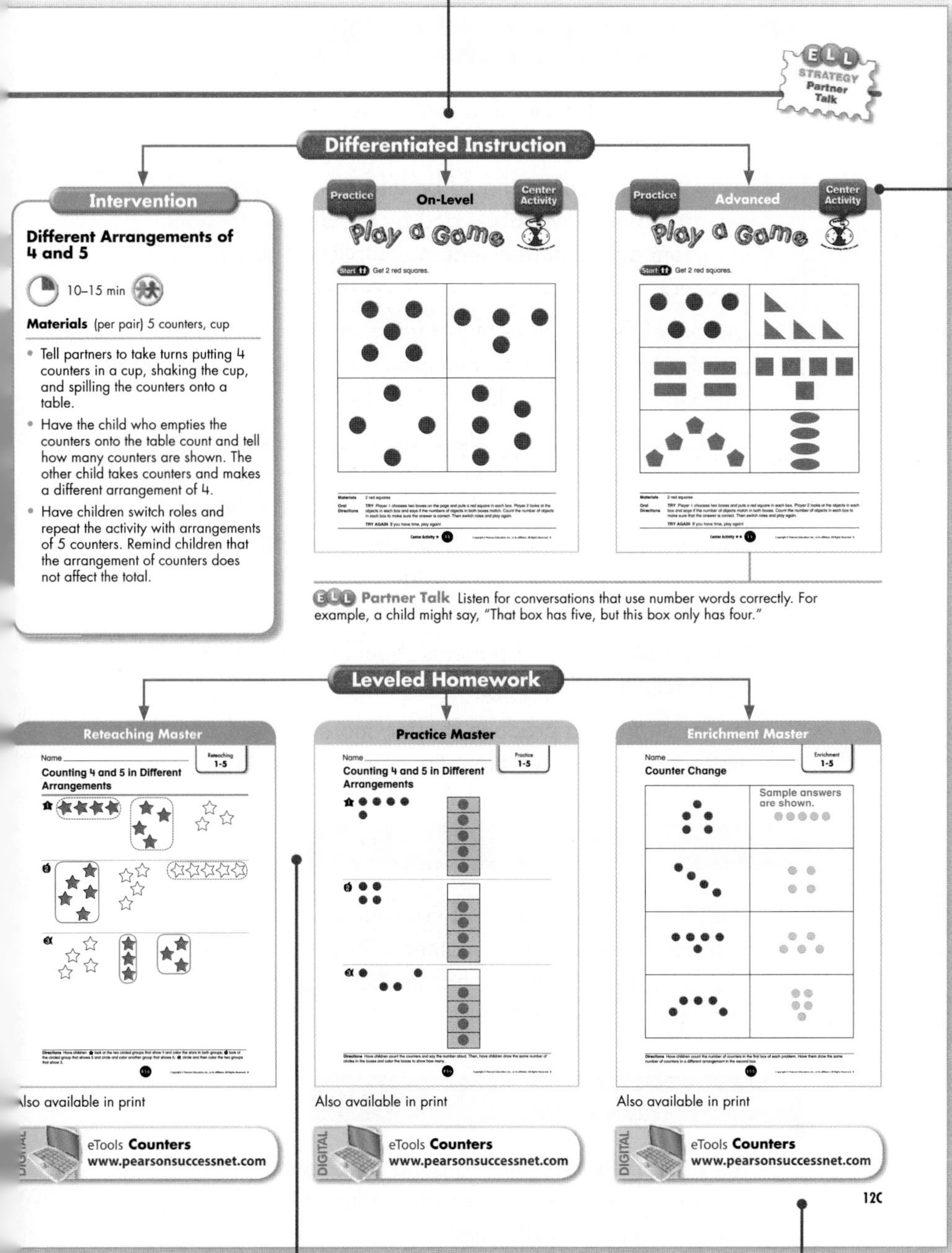

Data-Driven Differentiated Instruction

Assign your students the appropriate level of Intervention, Practice or Enrichment.

Center Activities

- **Ready-made** practice for every lesson.
- **Multiple uses**
  - Extend the activity by using the "If You Have More Time" feature
  - Ongoing review
  - Reuse year after year
- **ELL Strong ELL Strategies** encourage students to share their thinking.
- **Easy-to-manage, independent work** There are seven repeating activity formats.

The Center Activity formats are:

- **Clip and Cover** Students use number cubes and paper clips to select information. Students answer questions, cover answers in game spaces on a gameboard, and win when four spaces in a row are covered.
- **Display the Digits** Students answer questions, explain their thinking, and use number tiles to display their answers.
- **Quick Questions** Students toss number cubes, answer questions that have answers from 1 to 6.
- **Teamwork** Students each pick a number to determine which student will explain that numbered step in a multi-step process.
- **Think Together** Students are given a question and four answer choices. They each pick a number to determine who will discuss each answer choice.
- **Tic Tac Toe** Students toss number cubes, use an algebraic rule to compute with the numbers, and cover answers in game spaces on gameboards.
- **Toss and Talk** Students toss number cubes, explain how to answer a question next to the sum of the numbers, and win by getting connected rectangles on a four-by-four gameboard.

Leveled Homework

Leveled Homework promotes proficiency before End-of-Topic assessments.

Digital Resources

Digital Resources Include eTools, Games, and MindPoint Quiz Show.

Findings and Recommendations

The **National Mathematics Advisory Panel's Final Report** included the following findings and recommendations on topics that included instructional practices, materials, professional development, and assessments.

Core Principles of Math Instruction

- The areas to be studied in mathematics from pre-kindergarten through eighth grade should be streamlined and a well-defined set of the most important topics should be emphasized in the early grades. Any approach that revisits topics year after year without bringing them to closure should be avoided.
- Proficiency with whole numbers, fractions, and certain aspects of geometry and measurement are the foundations for algebra. Of these, knowledge of fractions is the most important foundational skill....
- Conceptual understanding, computational and procedural fluency, and problem-solving skills are equally important and mutually reinforce each other....
- Students should develop immediate recall of arithmetic facts to free the "working memory" for solving more complex problems.
- The benchmarks set forth by the Panel should help to guide classroom curricula, mathematics instruction, textbook development, and state assessments.
- More students should be prepared for and offered an authentic algebra course at Grade 8.
- Algebra should be consistently understood in terms of the "Major Topics of School Algebra," as defined by the National Math Panel.
- The Major Topics of School Algebra include symbols and expressions; linear equations; quadratic equations; functions; algebra of polynomials; and combinatorics and finite probability.

Effective Instruction Matters

- Teachers' regular use of formative assessments can improve student learning in mathematics.
- Instructional practice should be informed by high-quality research, when available, and by the best professional judgment and experience of accomplished classroom teachers.
- The belief that children of particular ages cannot learn certain content because they are "too young" or "not ready" has consistently been shown to be false.
- Explicit instruction for students who struggle with math is effective in increasing student learning. Teachers should understand how to provide clear models for solving a problem type using an array of examples, offer opportunities for extensive practice, encourage students to "think aloud," and give specific feedback.
- Mathematically gifted students should be allowed to accelerate their learning.
- Publishers should produce shorter, more focused and mathematically accurate mathematics textbooks....

Effective Assessment

- The National Assessment of Educational Progress (NAEP) and state assessments in mathematics should be improved in quality and should emphasize the most critical knowledge and skills leading to Algebra.

Importance of Research

- The nation must continue to build the capacity for more rigorous research in mathematics education to inform policy and practice more effectively.

NCTM Curriculum Focal Points and Connections

NCTM Curriculum Focal Points and Connections for Grade K
The set of three curriculum focal points and related connections for mathematics in Grade K follow. These topics are the recommended content emphases for this grade level. It is essential that these focal points be addressed in contexts that promote problem solving, reasoning, communication, making connections, and designing and analyzing representations.

Grade K Curriculum Focal Points

Number and Operations: Representing, comparing, and ordering whole numbers and joining and separating sets

Children use numbers, including written numerals, to represent quantities and to solve quantitative problems, such as counting objects in a set, creating a set with a given number of objects, comparing and ordering sets or numerals by using both cardinal and ordinal meanings, and modeling simple joining and separating situations with objects. They choose, combine, and apply effective strategies for answering quantitative questions, including quickly recognizing the number in a small set, counting and producing sets of given sizes, counting the number in combined sets, and counting backward.

Geometry: Describing shapes and space

Children interpret the physical world with geometric ideas (e.g., shape, orientation, spatial relations) and describe it with corresponding vocabulary. They identify, name, and describe a variety of shapes, such as squares, triangles, circles, rectangles, (regular) hexagons, and (isosceles) trapezoids presented in a variety of ways (e.g., with different sizes or orientations), as well as such three-dimensional shapes as spheres, cubes, and cylinders. They use basic shapes and spatial reasoning to model objects in their environment and to construct more complex shapes.

Measurement: Ordering objects by measurable attributes

Children use measurable attributes, such as length or weight, to solve problems by comparing and ordering objects. They compare the lengths of two objects both directly (by comparing them with each other) and indirectly (by comparing both with a third object), and they order several objects according to length.

Connections to the Focal Points

Data Analysis: Children sort objects and use one or more attributes to solve problems. For example, they might sort solids that roll easily from those that do not. Or they might collect data and use counting to answer such questions as, "What is our favorite snack?" They re-sort objects by using new attributes (e.g., after sorting solids according to which ones roll, they might re-sort the solids according to which ones stack easily).

Geometry: Children integrate their understandings of geometry, measurement, and number. For example, they understand, discuss, and create simple navigational directions (e.g., "Walk forward 10 steps, turn right, and walk forward 5 steps").

Algebra: Children identify, duplicate, and extend simple number patterns and sequential and growing patterns (e.g., patterns made with shapes) as preparation for creating rules that describe relationships.

Research Bibliography

Research Referenced in the Teacher's Editions

Baroody, A. J. *Children's Mathematical Thinking.* New York: Teacher's College, Columbia University, 1987.

Behr, M. J., Harel, G., Post, T., and Lesh, R. "Rational Number, Ratio, and Proportion." In D. A. Grouws (Ed.), *Handbook of Research on Mathematics Teaching and Learning* (1992), pp. 296–333.

Behr, M. J., I. Wachsmuth, T. R. Post, and R. Lesh. "Order and Equivalence of Rational Numbers: A Clinical Teaching Experiment." *Journal for Research in Mathematics Education,* 15 (1984), pp. 323–341.

Bell, A.W. "Diagnosing Students' Misconceptions." *The Australian Mathematics Teacher* 1 (1982): 6–10.

Black, P. and William, D. "Assessment and Classroom Learning." In *Assessment and Education.* Special Issue of Assessment in Education: Principles, Policy, and Practice. 5 (1) (1998): 7–75.

Booth, L. R. "Children's Difficulties in Beginning Algebra." In *The Ideas of Algebra, K–12.* Edited by A. F. Coxford, pp. 20–32. Reston, VA: National Council of Teachers of Mathematics, 1988.

Bright, G. W., and K. Hoeffner. "Measurement, Probability, Statistics, and Graphing." In *Research Ideas for the Classroom: Middle Grades Mathematics.* Edited by D. T. Owens, pp. 78–98. Reston, VA: National Council of Teachers of Mathematics, 1993.

Burns, M. "About Teaching Mathematics: A K–8 Resource." Sausalito, CA: Math Solutions Publications, 2000.

Carpenter, T., and E. Fennema. "Cognitively Guided Instruction: Building on the Knowledge of Students and Teachers." *International Journal of Educational Research.* Special Issue: The Case of Mathematics in the United States. W. Secada (Ed.), (1992), pp. 457–470.

Charles, R. *Math Across the Grades.* Boston: Pearson, 2005.

Cognition and Technology Group at Vanderbilt. "Looking at Technology in Context: A Framework for Understanding Technology and Education Research." *The Handbook of Educational Psychology,* D. C. Berliner and R. C. Calfee, eds. NY: Macmillan. (1996), pp. 807–840.

Cotton, K. "Monitoring Student Learning in the Classroom." Portland, OR, Northwest Regional Educational Laboratory. (2001).

Cuevas, G. J., P. H. Mann, and R. M. McClung. "The Effects of a Language Process Approach Program on the Mathematics Achievements of First, Third, and Fifth Graders." Paper presented at the meeting of the American Educational Research Association, San Francisco, CA (1986).

Dick, W., and L. Carey. *The Systematic Design of Instruction* (4th ed.). New York: Harper Collins College Publishers, 1996.

Diezmann and English. "The Roles of Representation in School Mathematics." Virginia: NCTM. (2003), p. 88.

Dreher, M. J. "Fostering Reading for Learning." In L. Baker, M. J. Dreher, and J.T. Guthrie (Eds.), *Engaging Young Readers: Promoting Achievement and Motivation* (2000), pp. 68–93.

Empson, Susan B. "Low-Performing Students and Teaching Fractions for Understanding: An Interactional Analysis." *Journal for Research in Mathematics Education* 34 (4) (2003), pp. 305–343.

Gagné, R. M. *The Conditions of Learning* (4th ed.). New York: Holt, Rinehart and Winston, Inc., 1977.

Graeber, A. O., and E. Tanenhaus. "Multiplication and Division: From Whole Numbers to Rational Numbers." In *Research Ideas for the Classroom: Middle Grades Mathematics.* Edited by D. T. Owens, pp. 99–117. Reston, VA: National Council of Teachers of Mathematics, 1993.

Hiebert, J. *Conceptual and Procedural Knowledge: The Case of Mathematics.* Hillsdale, NJ: Erlbaum, 1986.

Hiebert, J., and M. J. Behr. "Capturing the Major Themes." In *Number Concepts and Operations in the Middle Grades.* Edited by J. Hiebert and M. J. Behr, pp. 1–18. Hillsdale, NJ: Erlbaum; Reston, VA: National Council of Teachers of Mathematics, 1988.

Hiebert, J., T. P. Carpenter, E. Fennema, K.C. Fuson, D. Wearne, H. Murray, A. Olivier, and P. Human. *Making Sense: Teaching and Learning Mathematics With Understanding.* Portsmouth, NH: Heinemann, 1997.

Hong, H. "Effects of Mathematics Learning through Children's Literature on Math Achievement and Dispositional Outcomes." *Early Childhood Research Quarterly* 11 (4) (1996), pp. 477–494.

Kenney, P. A., and E. A. Silver, eds. "Results from the Sixth Mathematics Assessment of the National Assessment of Educational Progress." Reston, VA: National Council of Teachers of Mathematics, 1997.

Kilpatrick, Jeremy. *A Research Companion to Principles and Standards for School Mathematics.* Reston, VA: National Council of Teachers of Mathematics, 2003.

Kouba, V.L., C. Brown, T. Carpenter, M. Lindquist, E. Silver, and J. Swafford. "Results of the Fourth NAEP Assessment of Mathematics: Number, Operations, and Word Problems." *Arithmetic Teacher,* 35 (1988), pp. 14–19.

Kouba, V. L., and K. Franklin. "Multiplication and Division: Sense Making and Meaning." In *Research Ideas for the Classroom: Early Childhood Mathematics.* Edited by R. Jensen. New York: Macmillan Publishing Company, 1993.

Lodholz, R. D. "The Transition from Arithmetic to Algebra." In *Algebra For Everyone.* Edited by E.L. Edwards, Jr., pp. 24–33. Reston, VA: National Council of Teachers of Mathematics, 1990.

Mack, N. K. "Learning Fractions with Understanding: Building on Informal Knowledge." *Journal for Research in Mathematics Education* 21 (1990), pp. 16–32.

Martin, G. and Strutchens, M. E. (2000). "Geometry and Measurement" in E. A. Silver and P. A. Kenney (Eds.) *Results from the Seventh Mathematics Assessment of the National Assessment of Educational Progress* (pp. 193–234). Reston, VA: National Council of Teachers of Mathematics.

Mathematics Learning Study Committee. *Adding It Up: Helping Children Learn Mathematics.* Edited by J. Kilpatrick, J. Swafford, and B. Findell. Washington, D.C.: National Academy Press, 2001.

Mayer, R. E. "Models for Understanding." *Review of Research in Education,* 59 (1989), pp. 43–64.

Mayer, R. E., and M. C. Wittrock. "Problem-Solving Transfer." In D. C. Berliner and R. C. Calfee (Eds.), *Handbook of Educational Psychology* (1996), pp. 47–62.

National Council of Teachers of Mathematics. *Principles and Standards for School Mathematics.* Reston, VA: National Council of Teachers of Mathematics, 2000.

National Mathematics Advisory Panel. *The Final Report of the National Mathematics Advisory Panel.* Washington, DC: U. S. Department of Education, 2008.

Nesher, P. "Multiplicative School Word Problems: Theoretical approaches and empirical findings." In J. Hiebert and M. Behr (Eds.) *Number Concepts and Operations in the Middle Grades.* Reston, VA: NCTM (1988), pp. 162–181.

Payne, J. N., A. E. Towsley, and D. M. Huinker. "Fractions and Decimals" In Mathematics for the Young Child. Edited by J. Payne, pp. 175–200.
Reston, VA: National Council of Teachers of Mathematics.

Pesek, Dolores D., and David Kirshner. "Interference of Instrumental Instruction in Subsequent Relational Learning." *Journal for Research in Mathematics Education* 31 (5) (2000), pp. 524–540.

Pike, C. L. "The Use of Symbols, Words, and Diagrams as Indicators of Mathematical Cognition: A causal model." *Journal for Research in Mathematics Education,* 34 (2003), pp. 406–432.

Reys, B. J., and R. E. Reys. "Estimation-Directions from the Standards." *Arithmetic Teacher,* 37 (7) (1990), pp. 22–25.

Richards, D. D., and R. S. Siegler. "The Development of Time, Speed, and Distance Concepts." Paper presented at the Biennial Meeting of the Society for Research in Child Development (San Francisco, California, March 15–18, 1979).

Rittle-Johnson, B., and R. S. Siegler. "The Relation Between Conceptual and Procedural Knowledge in Learning Mathematics: A Review." In *The Development of Mathematical Skills.* Edited by C. Donlon, pp. 75–110. East Sussex, UK: Psychology Press, 1998.

Schwartz, D. L. and Heiser, J. "Spatial Representations and Imagery in Learning." In R. K. Sawyer (Ed.), *The Cambridge Handbook of the Learning Sciences* (2006), pp. 283–298.

Van de Walle, J. *Elementary and Middle School Mathematics.* Boston: Pearson, 2004.

Vye, N. J., D. L. Schwartz, J. D. Bransford, B. J. Barron, L. Zech, and Cognition and Technology Group at Vanderbilt. "SMART Environments That Support Monitoring, Reflection, and Revision." *Metacognition in Educational Theory and Practice.* D. Hacker, J. Dunlosky, and A. Graessner, eds. Mahwah, NJ: Erlbaum (1998).

Wearne, D., J. Hiebert, and S. Taber. "Fourth Graders' Gradual Construction of Decimal Fractions During Instruction Using Different Physical Representations." *Elementary School Journal,* 91 (4) (1991), pp. 321–341.

Wilson, P., and A. Osborne. "Foundational Ideas in Teaching About Measurement." In *Teaching Mathematics in Grades K–8: Research Based Methods.* Edited by T. Post. Boston: Allyn and Bacon, 1988.

MathStart® Bibliography

Books in the MathStart® Series

Animals on Board (Adding)
Beep, Beep, Vroom Vroom! (Pattern Recognition)
The Best Bug Parade (Comparing Sizes)
The Best Vacation Ever (Collecting Data)
Betcha! (Estimating)
Bigger, Better, Best! (Area)
Bug Dance (Directions)
Captain Invincible and the Space Shapes (Three-Dimensional Shapes)
Circus Shapes (Recognizing Shapes)
Coyotes All Around (Rounding)
Dave's Down to Earth Rock Shop (Classifying)
Dinosaur Deals (Equivalent Values)
Divide and Ride (Dividing)
Double the Ducks (Doubling Numbers)
Earth Day Hooray! (Place Value)
Elevator Magic (Subtracting)
Every Buddy Counts (Counting)
A Fair Bear Share (Regrouping)
Game Time! (Time)
Get Up and Go! (Timelines)
Give Me Half! (Understanding Halves)
The Greatest Gymnast of All (Opposites)
The Grizzly Gazette (Percentage)
Hamster Champs (Angles)
Henry the Fourth (Ordinals)
A House for Birdie (Understanding Capacity)
It's About Time (Hours)
Jack the Builder (Counting On)
Jump, Kangaroo, Jump! (Fractions)
Just Enough Carrots (Comparing Amounts)
Leaping Lizards (Counting by 5s and 10s)
Lemonade for Sale (Bar Graphs)
Less than Zero (Negative Numbers)
Let's Fly a Kite (Symmetry)
Mall Mania (Addition Strategies)
Mighty Maddie (Odd and Even Numbers)
Missing Mittens (Odd and Even Numbers)
Monster Musical Chairs (Subtracting One)
More or Less (Comparing Numbers)
One... Two... Three... Sassafras! (Number Order)
100 Days of Cool (Numbers 1–100)
A Pair of Socks (Matching)
The Penny Pot (Counting Coins)
Pepper's Journal (Calendars)
Polly's Pen Pal (Metrics)
Probably Pistachio (Probability)
Rabbit's Pajama Party (Sequencing)
Racing Around (Perimeter)
Ready, Set, Hop! (Building Equations)
Rodeo Time (Reading a Schedule)
Room for Ripley (Capacity)
Safari Park (Solving for Unknowns)
Same Old Horse (Making Predictions)
Seaweed Soup (Matching Sets)
Shark Swimathon (Subtracting 2-Digit Numbers)
Sluggers' Car Wash (Dollars and Cents)
The Sundae Scoop (Combinations)
Super Sand Castle Saturday (Measuring)
Spunky Monkeys on Parade (Counting by 2s, 3s, and 4s)
Tally O'Malley (Tallying)
3 Little Firefighters (Sorting)
Too Many Kangaroo Things to Do! (Multiplication)
Treasure Map (Mapping)

Glossary

1 fewer

1 more

2 fewer

2 more

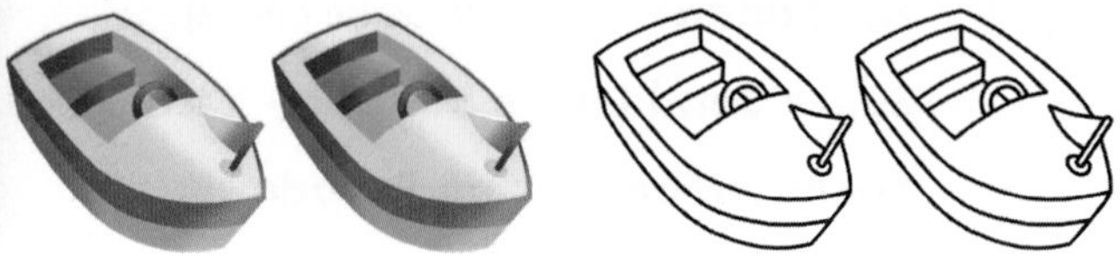

about the same

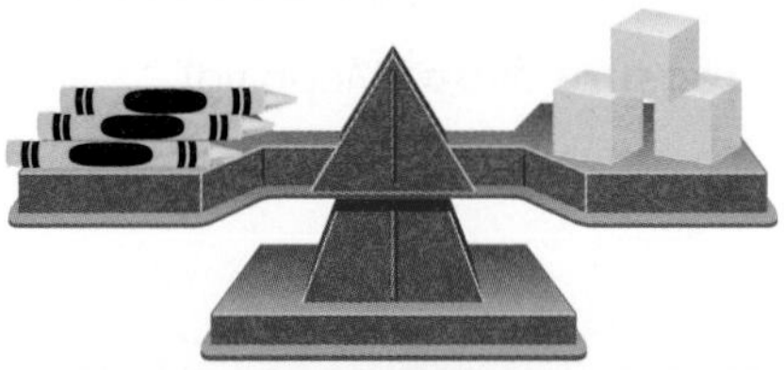

above (over)

add

3 + 2 = 5

addition sentence

$$4 + 1 = 5$$

as long as (same length as)

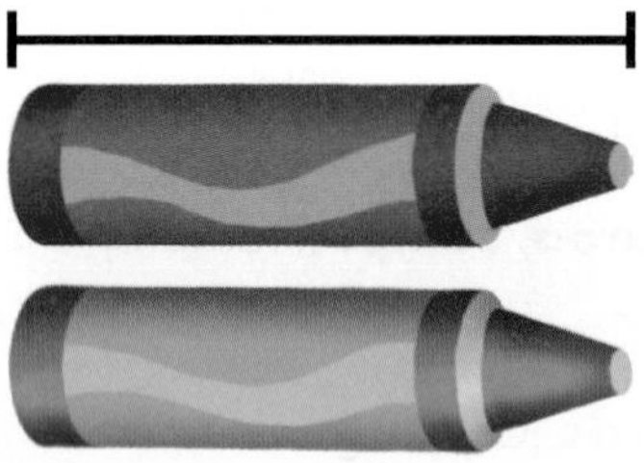

as many as

as short as

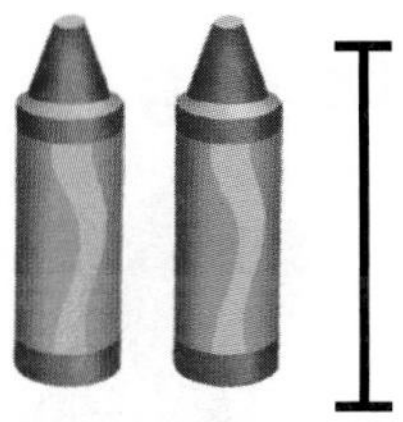

as tall as

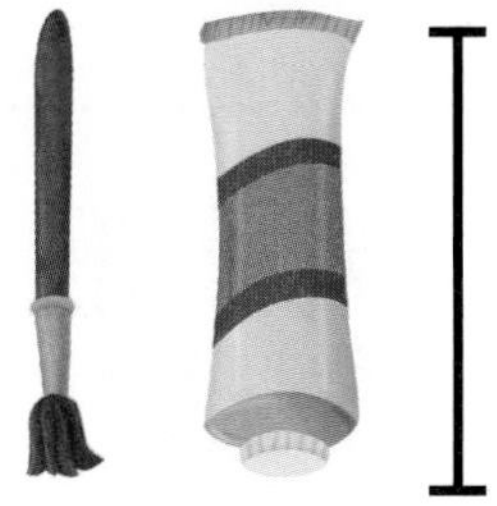

balance

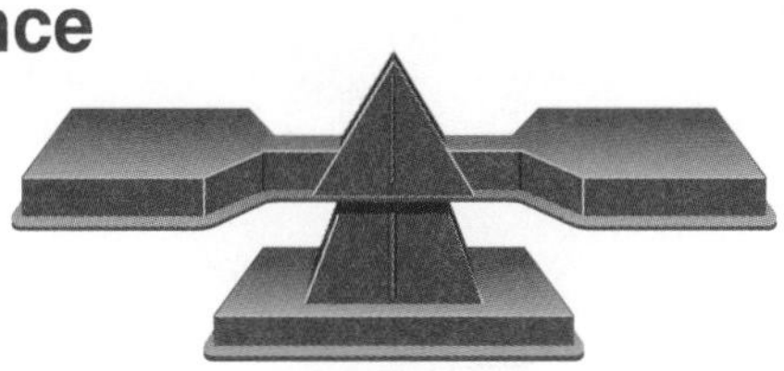

behind

below (under)

circle

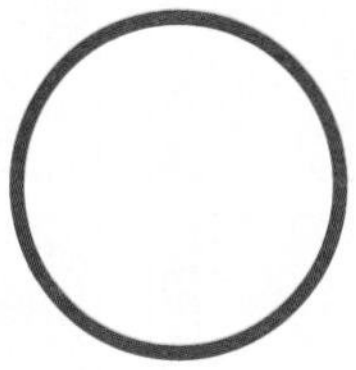

cone

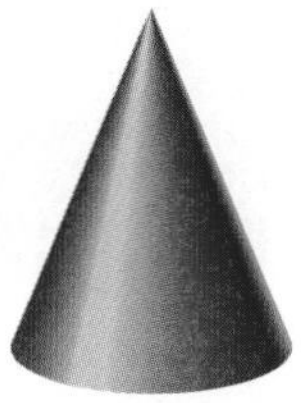

corner

count

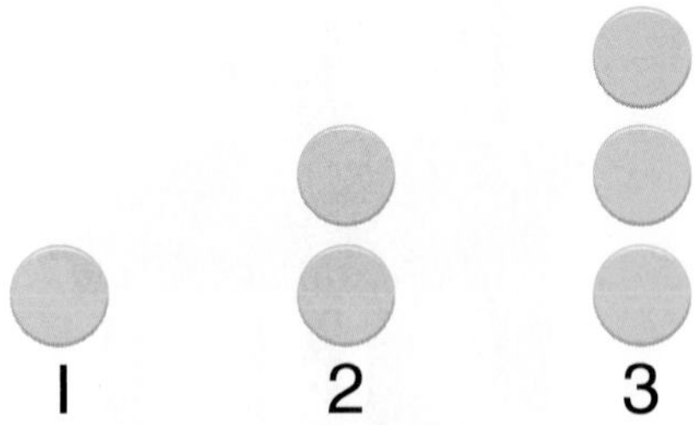

count by 10s

count by 2s

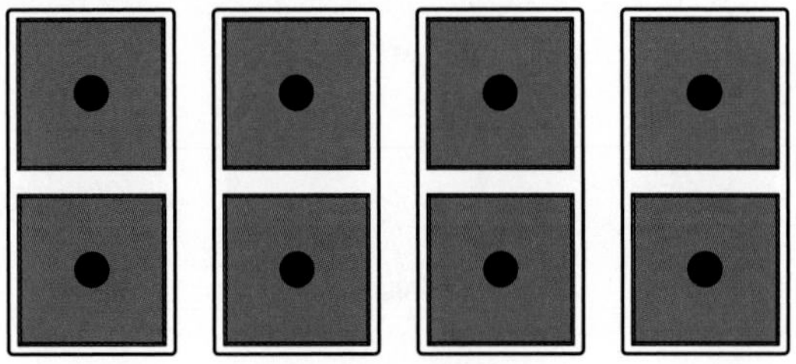

cube

cylinder

difference

$$8 - 3 = 5$$

different

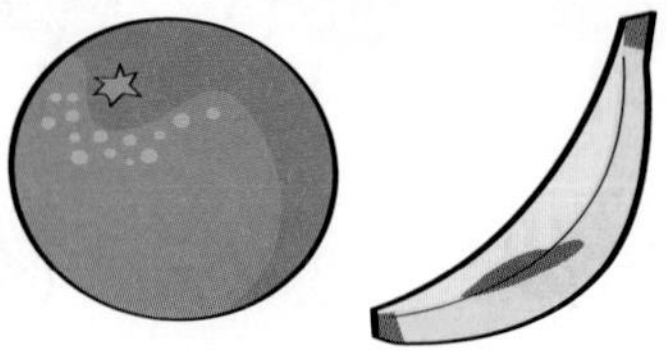

does not belong

edge

empty

equal sign

$$4 + 3 = 7$$

fewer

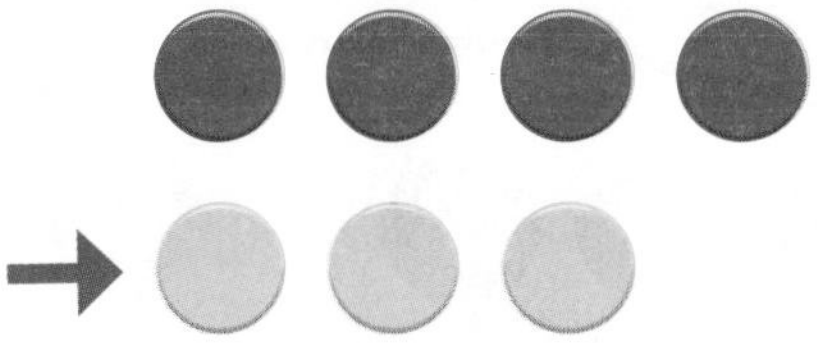

flat surface

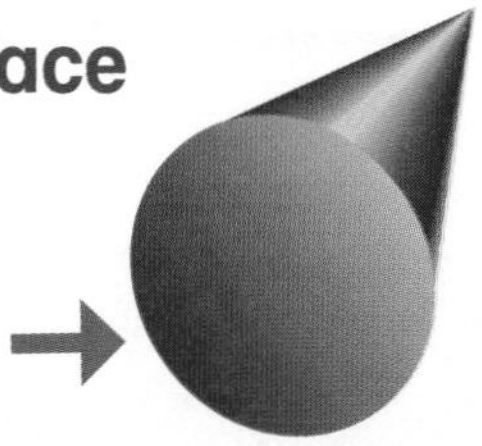

full

graph

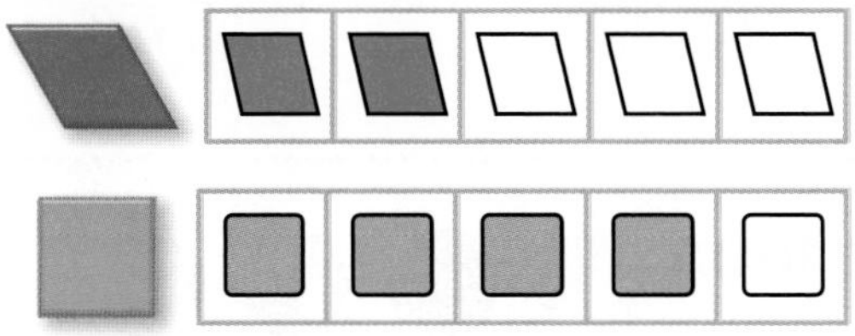

greater

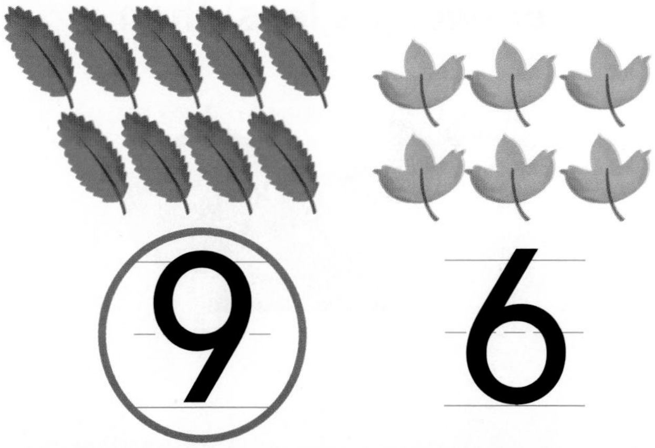

growing pattern

heavier (weighs more) than

hexagon

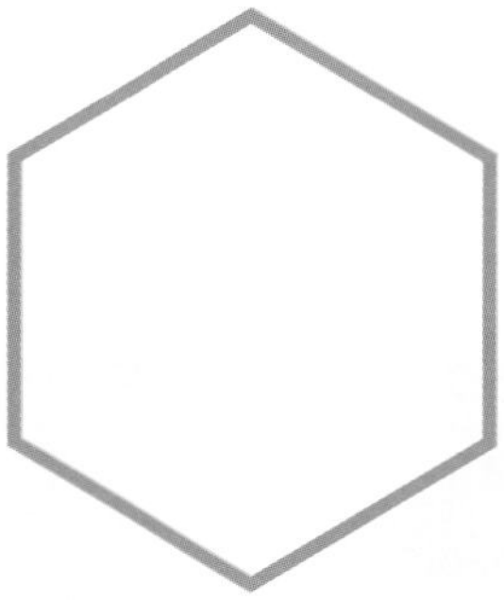

holds less

holds more

hundred chart

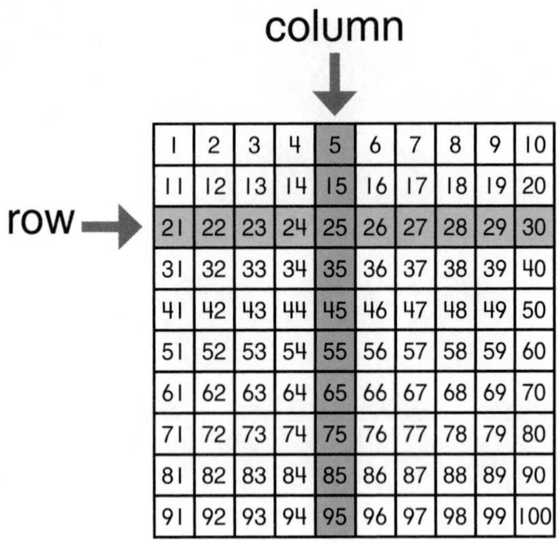

1	2	3	4	5	6	7	8	9	10
11	12	13	14	15	16	17	18	19	20
21	22	23	24	25	26	27	28	29	30
31	32	33	34	35	36	37	38	39	40
41	42	43	44	45	46	47	48	49	50
51	52	53	54	55	56	57	58	59	60
61	62	63	64	65	66	67	68	69	70
71	72	73	74	75	76	77	78	79	80
81	82	83	84	85	86	87	88	89	90
91	92	93	94	95	96	97	98	99	100

in front of

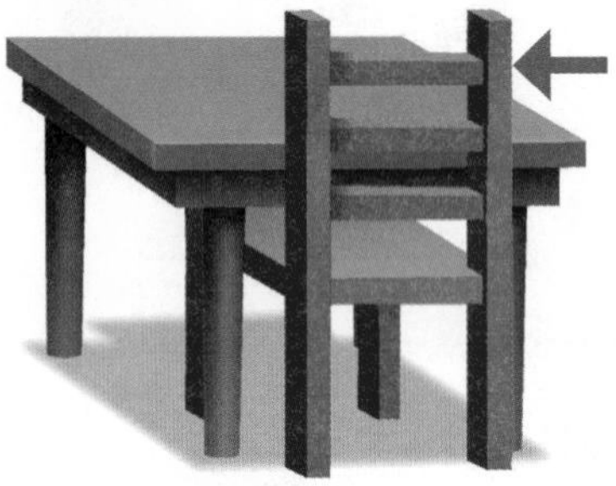

inside

join

least

left

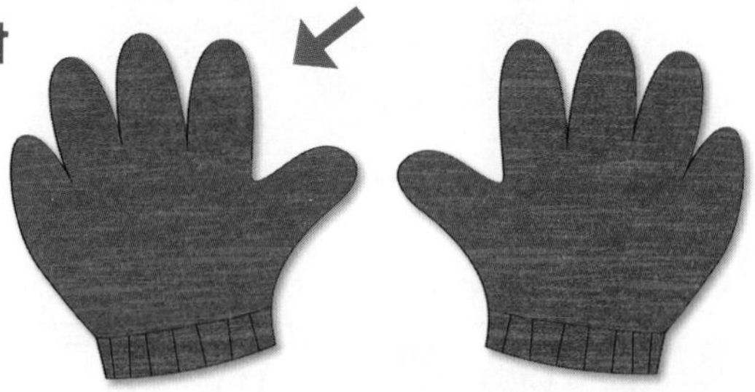

less than

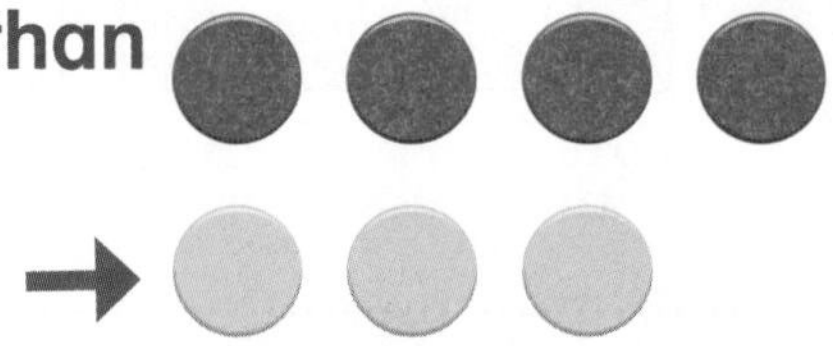

lighter (weighs less) than

Grade K • Glossary

longer than

longest

minus sign (−)

$$8 - 3 = 5$$

more than

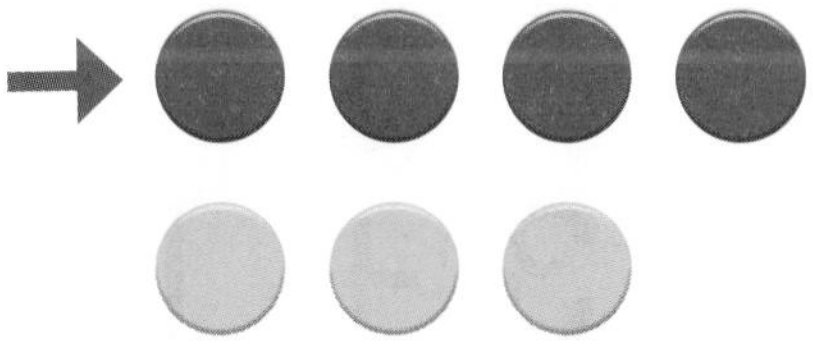

most

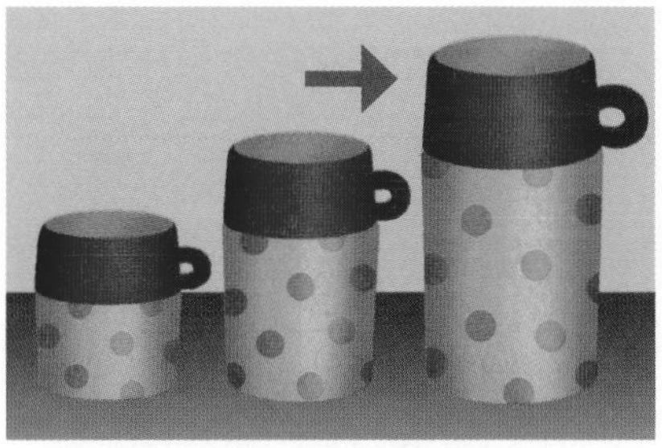

number line

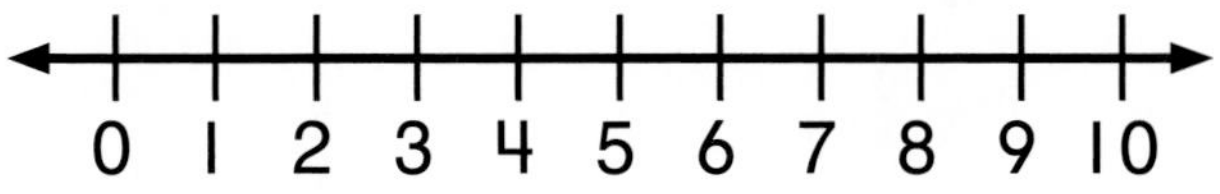

number story

1 and 3 is 4.

numbers

zero	0
one	1
two	2
three	3
four	4
five	5
six	6
seven	7
eight	8
nine	9
ten	10

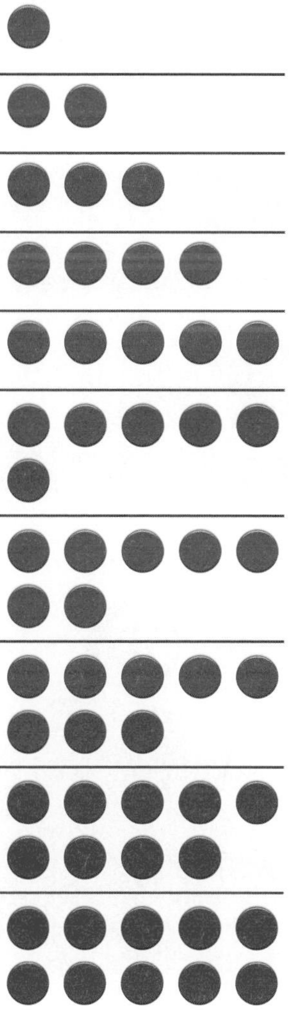

on (on top of)

order

0 → 1 → 2 → 3 → 4 → 5

outside

over

part

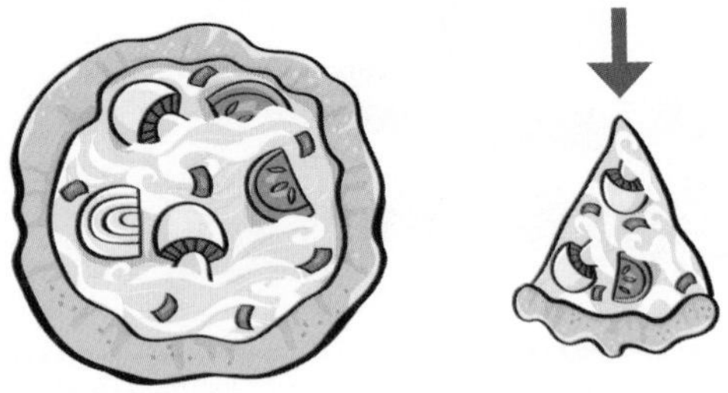

picture graph

Favorite Toys					
Top					
Yo-Yo					

plus sign (+)

$3 + 1 = 4$

real graph

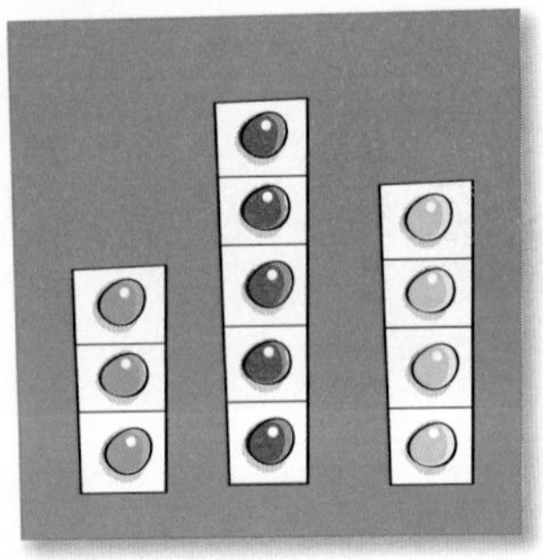

rectangle

right

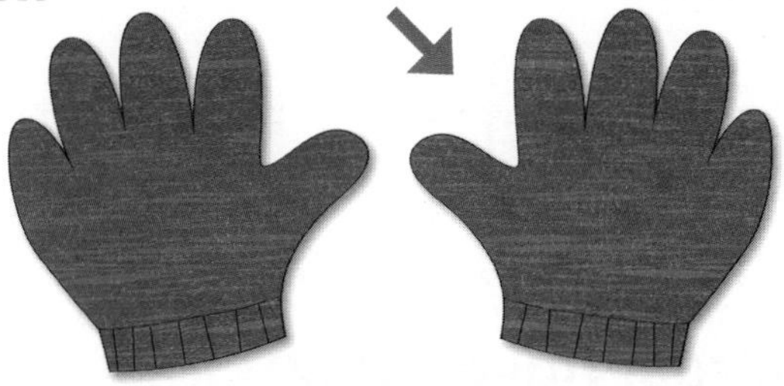

roll

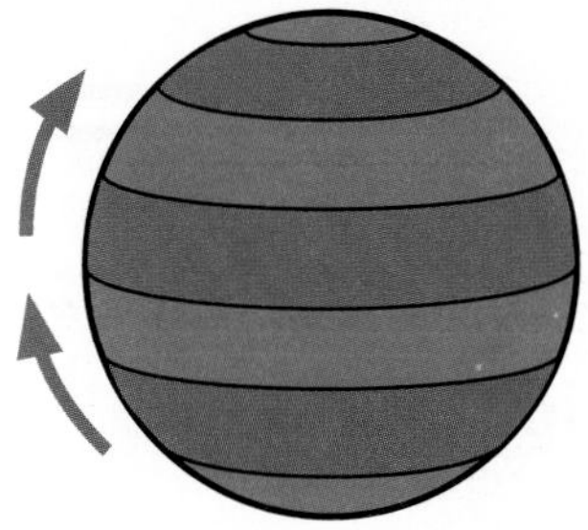

same

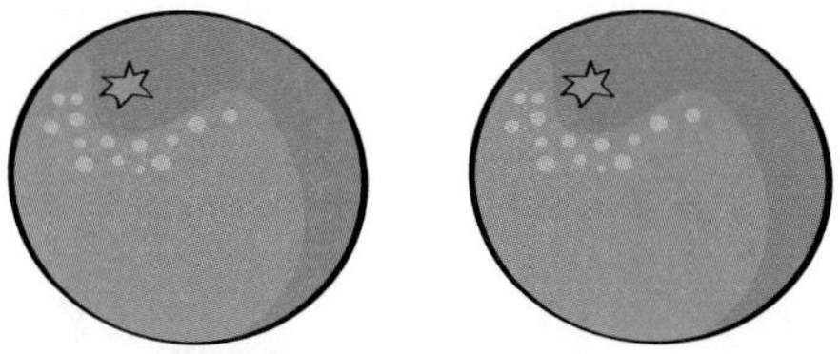

same number as

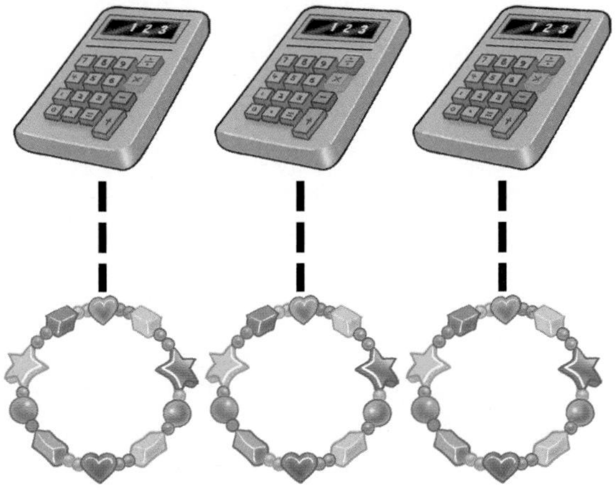

same shape

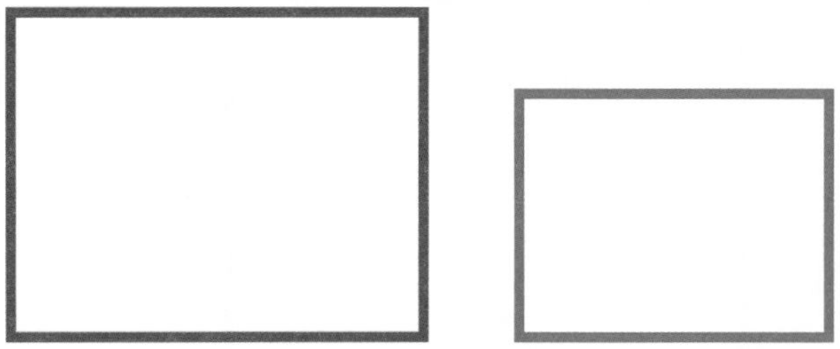

same size

shorter than

shortest

side

sort

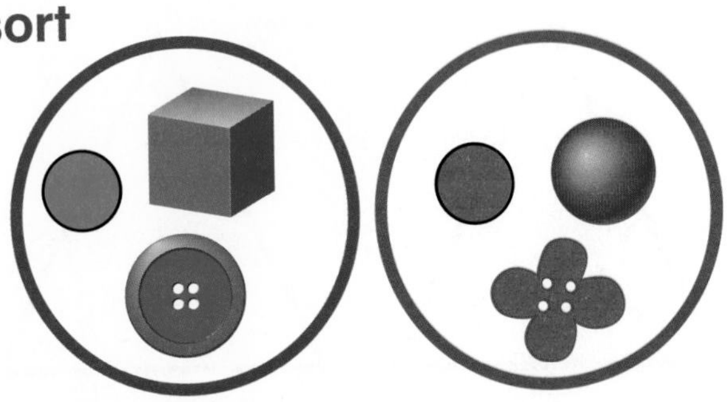

sphere

square

subtract (take away)

$3 - 1 = 2$

subtraction sentence

$3 - 1 = 2$

sum

$2 + 7 = 9$

Grade K • Glossary

taller than

tallest

triangle

under

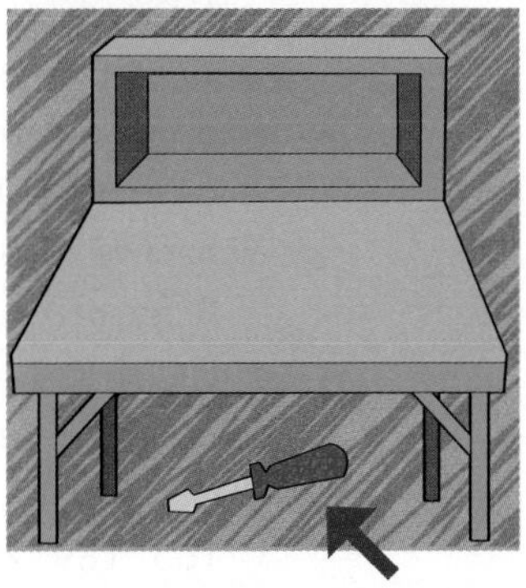

whole

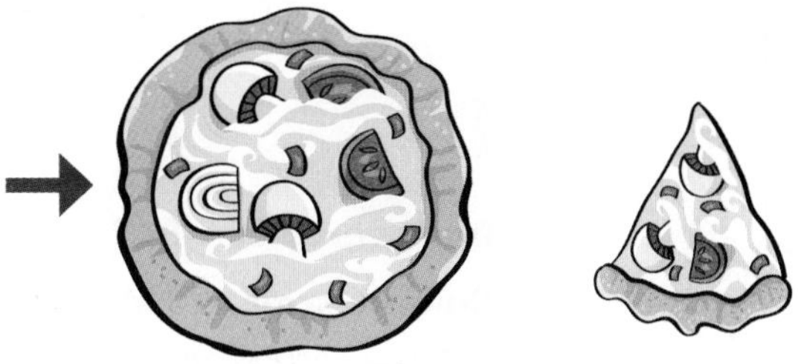

Index

T

V

W

Z

Notes

Notes